Laboratory Experiments in
MOTOR LEARNING

Second Edition

Lockhart *and* Johnson

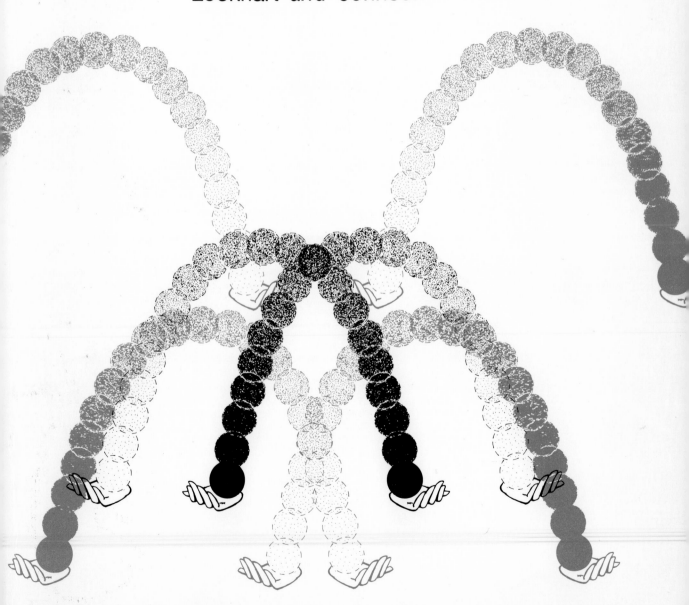

LABORATORY EXPERIMENTS IN MOTOR LEARNING

Laboratory Experiments
in
Motor Learning

Second Edition

Aileene S. Lockhart

Texas Woman's University, Denton

Joann M. Johnson

University of Minnesota, Duluth

KENDALL/HUNT PUBLISHING COMPANY

2460 Kerper Boulevard,
Dubuque, Iowa 52001

C   401662   02

80 00088

Contents

Preface

The purposes of a student laboratory are to encourage independence of thought, critical and creative growth, understanding of a process through which theories are formulated and, through these, the development of student involvement in the process of his own education. The experiments in this book, therefore, are designed not only to illustrate some basic principles of motor learning and to stimulate insightful understanding of concepts which have already been developed in this field of study, but it is hoped that they will also help to cause the student to ask questions, to think about how problems may be solved, and to develop the self-reliance, perspective, and inquisitiveness that will start him on the road to making his own discoveries. The stimulating instructor somehow conveys the excitement, the adventure, and the real spirit of research as well as the theoretical background and knowledges of his discipline. The laboratory to this instructor becomes an effective means to this end.

This book contains outlines for a few of the many laboratory studies in motor learning that have been developed by the senior author and by many named and unnamed graduate and undergraduate students who have patiently but eagerly inquired about the process of acquiring skill and improving motor performance. Over a period of at least twenty years these students have contributed ideas and equipment, often of their own devising, and in the process of testing and refining both, many have become skillful critics and creative contributors to physical education and coaching. Their joint and independent efforts and inquiries in and for the advancement of motor learning, as well as for their own growth, are appreciatively recognized.

The twenty laboratory experiences that have been chosen for inclusion herein are purposefully not complicated. It is assumed that these studies will be pursued by beginning students of motor learning, whether they be undergraduate or graduate. Very simple equipment is required in most instances. It is felt that wherever possible, however, students will also wish to be introduced to some of the devices which they may read about in research journals and in their textbooks. Consequently both types of equipment, varying from a simple ruler to some uncomplicated electromechanical instruments, are utilized in the conduct of these studies. In all cases the problem which is posed can be tackled, however, with different equipment and often with simpler equipment. "The Effect of Length of Set on Reaction Time," (Experiment 15), could better be studied with a reaction time-movement time instrument such as is illustrated in Experiment 2, but it is instructive to see so simple an approach to the problem as the lowly ruler (aided, of course, by Newton's far from lowly concept of the action of falling bodies). No doubt to students of physical education, "The Relationship Between Speed and Accuracy" is more convincingly and relevantly demonstrated with the electric tracking board, but the point can be explored with a paper and pencil test such as the one included in Experiment 12. The use of the free standing ladder and a dynabalometer are called for in Experiment 14. Since both of these tasks require dynamic balance, other measures of this same component may be substituted: stabilometer, Bass Circle test, bongo board. Experiment 1 involves juggling two tennis balls, about as simple an "apparatus" requirement as is possible; the acquisition of skill in learning, however, may be studied equally as well, following the same procedures, by using the free standing ladder, the pursuit rotor, the dynabalometer, the stabilometer or the bongo board. (A guide to construction and circuitry of much of the equipment used in the various experiments in this manual may be found in the Appendix. The numerical order of the experiments was designed to make the best use of the more sophisticated equipment, such as chronometers, interval timers, counters, and power supplies.)

It is necessary in the classroom laboratory to think ahead about all of the investigations one wishes to engage in and choose equipment with this in mind. After having learned how to solve the pyramid problem while investigating the effect of "The Sequence of Practice: Whole versus Part" (Experiment 20), for example, this particular device is of no further use as a possible piece of equipment by which to study massed versus distributed methods of practice (though it might serve well in a study concerned with the retention of problem-solving ability). Similarly, having "mastered" the pursuit rotor or mirror tracing while studying, let us say, bilateral transfer, these tasks can no longer be used as devices through which to learn about the early stages of skill acquisition.

Each of these experiments is opened with a brief introduction which gives the reader a very summary background about a large problem. A specific question is then posed. The materials required, and the procedures for conducting the exercise, are specified. Illustrative questions are given in a section entitled "Discussion and Inferences." These may be used in many ways. The instructor may require that the student write detailed asnwers to them; he may not require any formal report at all or may require that only some questions be answered; he may wish to supply his own questions; he may use the questions as the basis for oral rather than written reports; he may have the answers turned in to be graded or he may use these questions for discussion only; he and his students may occasionally stage a miniature "formal" research meeting at which laboratory findings are presented and discussed. Whatever procedure is used, it is important to have some kind of "post mortem" sessions so that questions can be asked, concepts can be discussed and understood, ideas can be verbalized and the relationships between theory and practice explored.

This manual includes "An Introduction to Laboratory Experiences in Motor Learning" in which concepts about motor learning itself, and in which the nature of motor learning laboratory tasks and equipment are discussed. Following this, information "For the Student" about how laboratory exercises should be conducted and how to prepare laboratory reports is presented. At the conclusion of that chapter is an important list of questions which should help the student in developing some basic concepts about motor learning and about research in general. So that data which are secured from the laboratory studies may be meaningfully interpreted, a review of "Basic Methods of Treating Data" is given.

Though students can discover much about learning as they pursue problems such as these in groups of only two or three persons, they will be able, of course, to make wider generalizations and place more confidence in what they find if more data can be made available. Despite (the very great) limitations which are posed by such a procedure, it is suggested that a Master Chart be posted on which all data from the members of the class or classes be posted.

Because the laboratory should provide supplementary learning and not mere duplication, it is hoped that the regular instructor will be able to conduct his own laboratory sessions. Laboratory assistants are definitely desirable and helpful; they should themselves have been participants in a motor learning laboratory prior to their involvement as motor learning laboratory assistants. Regardless of their excellence it is the regular instructor who can best keep the objectives of the various aspects of a motor learning course related to each other and clear to the students; it is he who can see that the student is not engaged in that which may seem to him to be two different courses one of which, though perhaps fun, is without seeming relevance to the other.

The motor learning laboratory envisioned by the present authors is not rigid in concept. The good laboratory, we believe, may appear to be quite the opposite, but it is a place where studies prove germinal, where creative possibilities abound, where the tools of observation and questioning and theorizing are effectively developed, where appreciation and respect for the investigator's work which appears in a very few pages in a scholarly journal are gained, and where imaginatively contributory research is sometimes stimulated. That at least some of these outcomes may stem from a student laboratory, not necessarily equipped with highly sophisticated instrumentation, *is* a definite possibility.

Denton, Texas   Aileene S. Lockhart
Duluth, Minnesota   Joann M. Johnson

An Introduction to Laboratory Experience in Motor Learning

Motor learning is learning the outcome of which is observed and evaluated chiefly in terms of relatively permanent changes in motor ability which result from practice and experience (rather than from maturational changes or from physiological-psychological fluctuations). Motor learning consists of the purposive integration of movements into effective patterns of action. It is instigated through the sense receptors, internal or/and external, integrated through the nervous system, and modulated through the response mechanisms into an end result which is organized, controlled movement. Thus motor learning obviously makes sensory, psychological and perceptual as well as motor demands. Since all voluntarily initiated motor learning involves the total being, it is perhaps redundant to speak in terms of sensori-motor or psycho-motor or perceptual-motor learning. These terms are often by-products of a perhaps unrecognized dualistic attitude toward learning; they should be used, however, when an investigator wishes to study or refer to one of these *specific* aspects of learning.

Though scientists are coming closer and closer to solving the mysteries which surround the exact process of learning, as yet performance must be used as an indication of that which has been learned. Learning and performance are not synonymous concepts however. Learning is not merely a change in behavior; it is a relatively permanent change, thus it is distinguishable from the widely observed, temporary fluctuations in performance. Performance is the demonstration of that which has been learned but a person does not always perform well, even though he has learned; he may be fatigued, he may be bored, he may be hampered by the conditions under which he is performing or by the equipment which he is using. Many transitory factors may interfere with performance.

How we learn and the conditions which affect performance are questions of universal interest, but motor learning is certainly of unique concern to physical educators and to physical and occupational therapists; movement, its quality and effectiveness, is the essence of physical education. To understand how people acquire motor skill and how motor performance can be improved have always been important objectives of physical education and coaching. Only recently, however, have students of these disciplines had the opportunity of studying in laboratory settings such things as the conditions under which motor learning progresses most effectively and smoothly, and the influence of various environmental conditions and physical components on motor performance. A course in motor learning has now become an established requirement for those who major in physical education and/or coaching and this study can be more meaningful if the student has the opportunity of investigating problems, of verifying conclusions for himself, and of understanding how problems are solved. This manual was written to provide laboratory experiences, an integral part of the learning process, for students who are enrolled in an introductory motor learning course.

REASONS FOR LABORATORY STUDY

Not all students immediately perceive the reasons for investigating motor learning in the laboratory. Why not on the field, on the court, in the gymnasium? The laboratory allows us to better control our observations. It is impossible to observe everything at once. It is impossible to untangle the many complex interrelationships which occur simultaneously during a game or even during practice. It is most difficult to perceive orderly relations when there are more of them than the observer can keep straight.

The acquisition of skill depends on the learner himself, the way he is taught, the way he practices, the conditions under which he practices, and the nature of the thing he is trying to learn. The learner's readiness to learn depends on his maturational level, his experiential background and his motivation. Since all of these variables operate at once, motor learning cannot be studied in any methodical way "on the field." In short, the field is an impractical place from which to attempt to investigate motor learning in any systematic fashion. In the laboratory it is possible to rearrange and/or to isolate some part of the world of movement in order to learn something about it. Much is lost in the highly complex conditions of our customary learning environment. The way to deal with complicated phenomena is to break them down. In the laboratory it is possible to examine predetermined aspects of learning and performance under controllable conditions and change variables in a prescribed way in an effort to discover lawful regularities. The laboratory setting provides experimental control. Systematic observation, control, and repeatability of circumstances are the chief reasons for taking motor learning problems to the laboratory.

Most certainly, the principles which explain learning in the research laboratory can be extended to serve as guides to the teacher or coach of motor activities. It should be understood, however, that motor learning research should not always be expected to result in immediately applicable, practical and specific implications for the teacher. In the laboratory associated with the classroom, many motor learning phenomena can be demonstrated. Motor learning as a discipline, on the other hand, is devoted to creating new knowledge and to developing a clearer understanding of the nature of learning. Not all such understanding is immediately related to the methodological aspects of instruction. Motor learning is not just another name for "methods of teaching" though, assuredly, it often does and should play a supportive role.

THE NATURE OF MOTOR LEARNING LABORATORY TASKS

The next perplexing problem relates to the nature of the tasks utilized in a motor learning laboratory. Why not study formalized patterns of movement which seem obviously relevant, such as spiking, serving and passing? If a person is interested in studying motor learning, it is necessary to start this study as closely to an unlearned level as is possible. Past experience may affect new learnings, either positively or negatively. New learning is built on and regulated by previous appropriate learnings; new learning is an extension and adaptation of already acquired ability. Consequently when studying learning, it is desirable to use unpracticed, unfamiliar tasks. Hence it is customary in the motor learning laboratory to employ so-called "novel" tasks, tasks that differ from those in the learner's usual repertoire of skills.

It is almost impossible to find or devise motor tasks which require none of the prior knowledge and skill which an adult learner has available to him but at least it is possible to start with unusual, unpracticed skills. It must be understood, however, that the real objective of laboratory experiments is never to learn to juggle, to improve one's performance on the ladder, the pursuit rotor, the star tracer or the stabilometer per se. These simply provide examples of learning. These are merely types of tasks which have been found useful in studying phenomena that occur in, or are related to, learning, such as retention, transfer and feedback; or the effect of stress, level of aspiration, or different distributions and lengths of practice on motor learning and on motor performance.

As previously noted, since we cannot observe learning directly, we must use performance as an indication of learning. We can observe performance during three arbitrary conditions of time: (1) *that which precedes performance*—the nature of the stimulus for performance, external or internal; the conditions which may affect the performance; the nature of the instructions given to the learner; and the learners themselves, their age, sex, background, and motivation; (2) *the performance itself*—the amount of time it takes; its quality, quantity, accuracy and repeatability; and (3) *the consequences of performance*—reward; reinforcement; feedback.

EQUIPMENT IN A MOTOR LEARNING LABORATORY

The performance itself is measured in the laboratory by objective means. Thus we may determine the accuracy of movement; the number of times something occurs; the number of mistakes made; the speed of movement; the amount of time it takes to complete a task or a part of a task in relation to the whole; the rate of response per unit of time; the amplitude of movement. Such measures require timers, counter, recorders, and so on.

For studies on motor learning it is necessary to have some means of presenting stimuli or presenting problems; some means of measuring the response; and some means of aiding the investigator in interpreting the data. You will find therefore in motor learning laboratories ways of presenting force, weight, and time; ways of measuring strength, flexibility, balance, reaction time, speed, accuracy and magnitude. You will find measuring equipment such as timers, stop watches and counters. You will find recorders, cameras, projectors, recordak machines, and claculators. In order to study learning, retention, interference and transfer, you will find many novel tasks, mirror tracing devices, mazes, rotary pursuit, and problem-solving devices.

All of this equipment can be classified according to type as, for example, *mechanical equipment*, such as depth perception apparatus, tensiometers, counters, mazes, motor development scales; *electrical equipment*, such as rotary pursuit apparatus, galvanic skin response, electric timers, counters and metronomes; and *pneumatic equipment*, such as dynamometers.

Equipment can also be classified as *perceptual motor*, such as reaction time devices, the Purdue Hand Precision apparatus, and the O'Connor Wiggly Blocks; *sensory motor equipment*, such as various discriminatory weights and forces, depth perception apparatus and kinesthesiometers; and psychophysiological equipment, such as knee reflex apparatus by which to demonstrate classical conditioning, the galvanic skin response instrument, and so on.

Because movement itself can also be categorized, it is possible to study the characteristics of different types of movement, using some of the above pieces of equipment; for example, *repetitive* type action, *serial* tracking movement, *positioning* and *continuous adjustive* movement.

Because learning is inferred from performance, because performance of motor tasks makes certain physical requirements, and because many of the components of motor proficiency are at least partly learned, a laboratory usually provides means of measuring *strength* (dynamometers, modified quadrants, strain gauges); *speed* and *reaction* time (velocity of propelled objects, reaction time-movement equipment, rho, velocitimer); *dexterity* (dynamic performance tests); *timing* (of movements and of moving objects); *balance*, both dynamic and static (dynabalometers, stabilometers, free standing ladders, stick tests); *steadiness* (tracing boards and steadiness testers); *accuracy* (pursuit rotors, Purdue Hand Precision); *perception* (weight, force, time and distance discriminators, kinesthesiometers; figural after-effect and accuracy of judgment equipment); *flexibility*, both dynamic and static; *coordination* (labyrinthian mazes, two hand star tracing apparatus); et cetera.

Any motor learning laboratory needs an adequate set of carpenter's and electrician's tools for much valuable equipment can be constructed, and all equipment needs occasional repair and adaptation for specific purposes: hammers, screwdrivers, saws; bit brace for use with drill and screwdriver; test light to trace circuits, fuses and lines; wrench and pliers; combination wire cutter and striper; jack knife, plastic tape, soldering gun and extension cords. Any laboratory needs a well-equipped first aid kit. Sophisticated equipment is certainly needed by some research workers in order to solve their problems, but, fortunately, the average classroom laboratory can be fairly well equipped in all cases where there is improvisational ability and ingenuity plus a few high speed clocks and counters. It is not necessary to have great financial backing to run a productive and stimulating motor learning classroom laboratory.

Although the studies included here may loosely be called "experiments," actually they are demonstrations from which it is hoped students will come to more fully understand some of the established motor learning concepts and some of the questions and problems which have directed the efforts of motor learning scholars. The equipment required to conduct the demonstrations included in this book is purposely modest in amount and cost. It does include, purposely, some devices which have been repeatedly utilized in motor learning studies because they have been proven to be suitable for such research. Even where more sophisticated instrumentation is available it is instructive for students to see that investigation and an inquisitive point of view may flourish despite the lack of large research funds and formal contracts.

For the Student

The studies in this book have been prepared to introduce you to some motor learning problems and questions, and to help you to understand some of the concepts which have developed about this subject. Some of these are also alluded to briefly in the section on "Laboratory Experience in Motor Learning." Refer to those pages often.

Each of the studies in this book has a purpose. First, read the introductory remarks which accompany each experiment and try to *understand the reason* for each experiment. Think about why each experiment is included, what you are trying to discover and, in each case, what you should observe. Then read the directions carefully and *follow the procedures exactly*. You should do these things for yourself, not depending on other classmates who may already have completed an experiment to tell you what it is about and what to do. *Do your own reasoning, reading and understanding.* It is most important, too when you are the subject for you to try to *do your best on each trial* of each experiment. If you do not, your data will demonstrate nothing. Subjects who are not willing to exert their maximum efforts and who are reluctant or unwilling to continue when conditions become uncomfortable are poor subjects. By the same token, though it is realized that many students of motor learning seem to be a highly competitive lot, some of the equipment is delicate and requires proper use. Do not abuse the equipment in all-out (and perhaps inappropriate) efforts to "beat" your classmates.

You will find that you will be more comfortable and will be able to perform best if you are dressed appropriately. Some of the experiments require active and large movement. Proper footgear is often of utmost importance.

The data you secure will be more meaningful if they can be supplemented with the records of your classmates. Probably your instructor will request you to record your data on a Master Chart so that all of it will be available to all students. It is important to have sufficient data. You may not be able to observe certain phenomena unless you have a sufficiently wide and representative sample of subjects and scores. While considering these data you will be impressed with a most significant fact, that of the great inter and intra individual differences which exist within and among people.

Obviously if data are to be used collectively it is imperative that they be presented in the same form and that no deviations in procedure be made by any of the "experimenters" or "subjects." Even so you will want to discuss in class sometime the limitations imposed by this method of securing data and the cautions you must observe when interpreting such data.

SAFETY

Be particularly concerned with the safety of the subject. In any case, for example, where a subject could fall, "spot" him (as when he is on the stabilometer, the dynabalometer or the free standing ladder).

When you are ready to begin, if the apparatus or equipment required to conduct your experiment has not already been assembled and positioned for you, *seek help* from the instructor or laboratory assistant, particularly in all cases where electrical circuitry is involved.

Be sure that there is enough space around you so that your operations will not endanger other experimenters or subjects, and so that you can proceed unhampered by them.

CARE OF EQUIPMENT

Though you should enjoy conducting and participating in these studies and though it is hoped that you will find the laboratory experience stimulating and interesting, remember that stop watches, styluses, switch mats, counters, interval timers, chronometers and the like are *not toys*, but rather are amazingly expensive and sometimes fragile instruments often housed in breakable containers and cases. Please handle them carefully and use them only for their intended purposes. The laboratory is no place for horseplay. It is a good place to develop professional attitude and to learn something about the spirit of research.

THE CONDUCT OF LABORATORY STUDIES

1. Work with partners unless otherwise indicated. You will notice the abbreviations S and E in the procedural explanations which follow; these refer respectively to the "subject" (S) and to the "experimenter" (E). If you are first the subject in one experiment, reverse roles with your partner so that you become, in the subsequent exercise, the experimenter first.

2. Each study is presented with a brief introduction and a statement of the purpose of the experiment so you will be oriented with reference to the question. Read this material carefully and do not proceed until you understand the nature of the problem. *Why* is it a problem and what is its significance?

3. What is required? Secure the materials that are necessary before you start.

4. *Read the section on procedure with care and do not proceed until you understand exactly what you are to do, why you are doing it, and how the apparatus or equipment works.* Avoid errors by thinking through the whole problem *before* proceeding (you cannot rectify errors later on). Obtain answers to your procedural questions before you start. Then if you follow the instructions you should obtain accurate, reliable results.

5. The E conducts the study, carefully following the directions, and records the S's results on the appropriate score sheet in the S's laboratory manual. The S then becomes the E and the E the S.

6. Make a note of observations, questions, hunches, discrepancies, evaluations and possible applications as you proceed so you will not forget them. It is bad practice to trust your memory about such things.

7. Turn in your scores to the instructor or record them, if you have been so directed, on the class Master Data Chart.

8. Call the instructor's or assistant's attention to any nonfunctioning instrument.

9. Help put apparatus and equipment away when you are through with them.

10. Secure all data gathered by members of your class (as recorded on Master Data Charts). Organize these data and analyze the findings. In order to "make sense" of the various scores and be able to interpret them, you will need to arrange them in some meaningful manner. Graphic presentation is often helpful (tables, curves, graphs). Simple statistical treatment is usually called for (see section on "Basic Methods of Treating Data").

PREPARATION OF LABORATORY REPORTS

1. Having studied the introductory remarks and subsequently secured the data and arranged the scores and your observations into some systematic form, and listed your findings, it is hoped that you are now ready to read more about the subject of the experiment. References related to each problem are presented at the end of each experiment; these will give you background information. Ask your instructor for further reading on topics which particularly interest you. Compare what you and your classmates found with other facts which you know or can find out about the subject.

2. Independently of your partner or classmates answer the questions which are posed in each section labelled "Discussion and Inferences" in the spaces provided for this purpose. Use additional paper if needed. Put your name and the date on each sheet and turn your report in to your instructor. Always include the data from which you made your conclusions.

3. Your instructor may ask you to compile into a laboratory notebook all descriptions of laboratory experiments, your data and your notes. In this case, in whatever way is meaningful to you (unless directed otherwise), indicate the meaning—the significance—the relationships of the observation which you have made and the results which you have found. You may summarize and synthesize. You may make comments regarding individual experiments. You may use your own results and those of your classmates which are posted on the bulletin board in the laboratory or perhaps you may augment these results with those of students from previous classes which might be posted; you may refer to any books or sources. In other words, this will be *your* notebook. Use your own ingenuity, your own imagination, your own meanings in completing this assignment. You may wish to concentrate your efforts and go "all out" on just a couple of the experiments, with briefer notes on the others.

4. You will not now be able to answer all of the following questions, certainly not in relation to each experiment, but as you reconsider these matters from time to time you will find that you can do so more satisfactorily and that you are developing some important basic concepts about motor learning and about research.

   a. Why is it extremely important to follow laboratory instructions implicitly? What difference would it make if you did not?

   b. Can you suggest reasons which might explain why you have been instructed to alternate roles as "subject" and "experimenter" with your partner?

   c. How might you characterize a "good observer"?

   d. Criticize constructively the experiments themselves, their limitations, approach, purpose and significance.

   e. What is meant by "control" and "a control," and the values thereof?

   f. What practical applications of phenomena that you have observed have you been able to formulate?

   g. What can you say about the general quality of your own motor performance? Did you find consistencies or variations in your abilities throughout the course as you participated in these experiments? How can you explain your answers?

   h. What is meant by reliability? Of what importance is it? What efforts were made to secure reliability in each experiment? What did you and your partner do to improve "subject reliability" and the reliability of your judgment?

   i. What is meant by objectivity? Of what importance is it? What efforts were made to secure objectivity? How are objectivity and reliability related? Are the terms synonymous?

j. Would you consider it worthwhile to take all of the scores made by all of the subjects on any one experiment (as your laboratory experiments were conducted) and use them as the basis for listing findings and deriving conclusions for an article you hope to have published? If not, exactly why not?

k. Are findings and conclusions the same thing? How do they differ? What relationship should there be between them? What relationship should exist between the conclusion and the purpose?

l. What experiment or experiments demonstrated a point most effectively to you? Why do you think this occurred?

m. What concepts have you derived as a result of your experiences in the laboratory?

n. What is meant by a plateau, physiological limit, psychological limit, methodological limit? How might these be related to performance? to learning?

o. What generalizations can you make that you feel are justifiable regarding motor learning?

p. Compare learning curves drawn from the results of different experiments. How can you explain what you found?

q. Based on your laboratory experiences what can you say about trial and error learning, insightful learning, problem solving learning?

r. Have you experienced examples of interference in learning?

s. Describe the effects of practice on performance and on learning.

t. What is the effect of an interpolated similar task on subsequent performance of the initial task?

u. Discuss the significance of your results; how do your results compare with those found by other investigators?

v. In what study do you think the purpose and procedure were best? Why?

w. Do you think any factor or factors other than the one studied in any of the experiments might have accounted for your results?

x. Look at the statement of the problem, then at your conclusion. Did the study, through your efforts, "deliver" what was promised?

y. Why is there a generally accepted form for reporting the results of investigations?

z. Have you thought about the ethics of investigation?

Basic Methods of Treating Data

If the results obtained from the experiments you conduct and/or participate in are to be meaningfully interpreted, it will be necessary to organize and summarize the data you secure. There are certain basic methods of treating these data. The intent here is merely to present samples of some basic techniques that are applicable when working with the type of data you will collect in the laboratory. It is hoped that you have already had a course in basic statistics; in this event the material in this chapter will constitute only a brief review for you. If you have not, this in no way means that you cannot learn to ask very good questions, and you can begin now to learn what to do with quantitative data. The subjects touched upon here are by no means the only ones that you should be familiar with in order to really understand the research in motor learning and motor performance. It is hoped that you will be sufficiently curious to begin to study the interesting tools of data analysis.

Consistent and accurate methods of collecting and recording data are very important. When data collected by different investigators (as in the case of these laboratory studies) are used to make inferences or draw conclusions, extreme caution must be used. Only when each investigator exercises great care, follows the directions given in each experiment exactly and makes accurate measurements will the data so collected be of any real value. If this is done, however, such data should provide a means of demonstrating various phenomena related to motor learning. If the laboratory experiments described in this book were conducted for purposes of serious research, many changes in methodology would have to be effected so that valid and defensible conclusions could be drawn. It would be instructive for students to discuss changes that would be required before any of these "experiments" could merit the term "research."

NOTATION

Unfortunately, statisticians do not agree on the symbols they use in analyzing data. Their "shorthand" is fearsome looking to the uninitiated but the statistician's language, like any other foreign language, becomes easy to interpret with practice. There is no need to be awed by formulae; anyone who can add, subtract, multiply and divide can understand and carry out the fundamental processes required by elementary statistics. Following are some of the symbols most frequently used:

$$\bar{X} = \text{the arithmetic mean or M, the average}$$
$$\Sigma = \text{Greek capital letter Sigma, meaning "the sum of"}$$
$$X \text{ (or Y)} = \text{a raw score in a series of measures}$$
$$N = \text{number of subjects, measures or parameters}$$
$$f = \text{the frequency with which a raw score (X or Y) occurs}$$

SD	=	standard deviation, also indicated by the Greek letter σ or written as *sigma*; indicates how data are grouped about or dispersed from the mean
r	=	coefficient of correlation
σ^2 or SD^2	=	the variance, the square of the standard deviation
x (or y)	=	a deviation score (for example $\overline{X} - X = x$)

MEASURES OF CENTRAL TENDENCY

"What is the average?" "How do I compare with the group?" The questioner is asking for a means by which he can evaluate performance. We all understand batting and bowling averages. In a simple quick summary these numbers tell us what to expect "on the average." To answer questions which call for a representative score some measure of central tendency has to be obtained. All averages are called "measures of central tendency" by statisticians and the ones they find most useful are the mean and the median.

The mean. The mean is the arithmetic or common average of a set of scores. The notation looks like this and it tells us simply to add all the scores together and divide by the number of cases:

$$\overline{X} = \frac{\Sigma X}{N} \qquad \text{Mean} = \frac{\text{the sum of the raw scores}}{\text{the number of scores collected.}}$$

Let us assume that we wish to find, for example, the mean of a subject's scores made in Experiment 15, "The Effects of Length of Set on Reaction Time." Raw scores for one subject on each of the fifteen trials might be as follows, ranging from .08 (the lowest score) to .20 (the highest score):

Trial	Score
1	.10
2	.16
3	.12
4	.13
5	.18
6	.20
7	.08
8	.09
9	.12
10	.13
11	.14
12	.11
13	.10
14	.10
15	.10
Σ (total)	1.86

$$\overline{X} = \frac{\Sigma X}{N} \quad \frac{\text{total of raw scores}}{\text{number of scores}}$$

$$= \frac{1.86}{15}$$

$$\overline{X} = .124 \quad \text{(the average or mean made by this subject)}$$

The median. The score above which half of all scores occur and below which half of all scores occur is the median. It is the fiftieth percentile of any group of scores. To calculate the median, all raw scores are placed in rank order and the score that appears exactly in the middle of this list is the median score. The median of the data previously presented, for example, is .12.

The scores are listed below in rank order:

.08	
.09	
.10	
.10	
.10	
.10	
.11	
.12	median (Md) or 50th percentile
.12	
.13	
.13	
.14	
.16	
.18	
.20	

Use of measures of central tendency. In a perfectly normal distribution the mean, the median and the mode (the most common score) are identical. Most distributions, however, are not perfectly normal. There are reasons why one might choose, in these cases, one measure of central tendency instead of another. The mean is affected by the *size* of every score while the median is influenced only by the *position* of scores in a distribution. If the subject's scores in the above experiment had been .08, .09, .10, .10, .10, .10, .11, .12, .12, .13, .13, .14, .16, .70, .90 (note the only changes are in the last two scores), the median still would be .12 (its middle position is unchanged by the size of the substituted scores). The mean, however, would be affected by the value of the quite atypical scores and would change to .205. The most frequently employed measures of central tendency is the mean. It usually is more stable (tends to vary less from one sample to another) and can be used more meaningfully in connection with further calculations.

Where there are many scores, methods other than the simple counting used above are employed in computing means and medians. Scores are grouped into class intervals and by using appropriate computational techniques measures of central tendency can be determined much more easily than is possible by "counting" procedures.

THE STANDARD DEVIATION

Standard deviations are used to describe the distribution of scores in relation to means on any parameter by comparing them to normally distributed scores. They tell the statistician in a very compact way how scores are dispersed about means, how scores vary from means, how scores are spread in the distribution. Since scores made on tests of physical abilities often tend to be normally distributed, the standard deviation is an important concept to understand when dealing with data of this type.

The word "standard" in standard deviation refers to the mean as a "standard." The mean $(\overline{X})$ is the criterion or standard to which all other scores are compared. The "deviation" of the standard deviation refers to the difference between each individual's score and the mean $(\overline{X}\text{-}X)$. In calculating the standard deviation the results are squared. This accomplishes at least two things: (1) it eliminates negative scores and (2) it gives greater proportionate weight to scores that vary greatly from the mean. To obtain the standard deviation when you are dealing with few scores and ungrouped data (1) arrange the scores (x) vertically as obtained, (2) total all these scores (Σx), (3) divide ΣX by N to obtain the mean $(\overline{X})$, (4) calculate the deviation from $\overline{X}$ of each x (d), (5) square the d (d^2), (6) obtain the sum of d^2 (Σd^2), (7) apply appropriate formula:

$$SD = \sqrt{\frac{\Sigma d^2}{N-1}}$$

Example

X	d	d^2		
22	8	64		
21	7	49	$SD = \sqrt{\dfrac{\Sigma d^2}{N-1}}$	
16	22	4		
15	1	1		
14	0	0	$SD = \sqrt{\dfrac{200}{9}}$	
14	0	0		
10	−4	16	$SD = \sqrt{22.22}$	
10	−4	16		
9	−5	25	$SD = 4.7$	
9	−5	25		

$$\Sigma X = 140$$
$$N = 10$$
$$\overline{X} = 14$$
$$\Sigma d^2 = 200$$

Knowing the standard deviation is invaluable when trying to understand a score. In general terms, the smaller the measure of dispersion in relation to the measure of central tendency (the mean, or the median), the more clustered or concentrated is the distribution, and the larger the measure of dispersion the greater is the scattering or dispersion of the scores away from the central tendency. Thus a sample is homogeneous if the standard deviation is small, and heterogeneous if the standard deviation is large.

Suppose in Experiment 9 on the "Effect of Knowledge of Results on Performance" the data for one S indicated that he tended to vary +6°. Another S may have tended to vary +16°. What do these scores mean? Without further information little can be inferred. If, however, group data from this experiment had revealed that the mean was +10° and the standard deviation was 8°, for example, then it could be inferred that both of the above scores would fall within one standard deviation of the mean; they are both within the concept of the term "average."

Further discussion of standard deviation may make interpretation of such raw data more meaningful. It is known, for example, that if the data collected from any source are normally distributed and there are enough of them, then scores which fall within one standard deviation on either side of the mean will include about two-thirds of all of the cases.

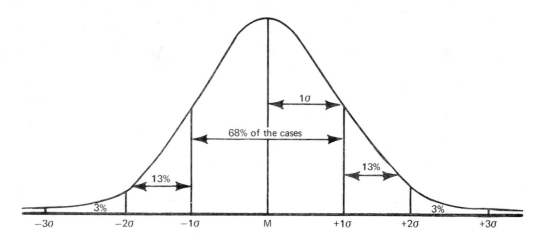

A normal distribution, mean, standard deviations and approximate percentages within one sigma units.

Only one-sixth of all scores, therefore, will fall more than one standard deviation above and only one-sixth more than one standard deviation below the mean. Scores reaching such limits are significant because they differ greatly from the average. With a mean of 10° and a standard deviation of 8°, as in the above example, scores of 1° and 2° or more than 18° can be interpreted as being quite different from scores of 6° or 16°. The standard deviation can also be described as the "moment of inertia" where the distance the distribution of the mass is from the center of rotation is the important factor. (This value is also squared in computations). The standard deviation does not reveal subtle differences between scores, but it does describe, in general terms, the nature of raw data.

CORRELATION

Significant information is often gained when a relationship between measures is discovered. This necessitates having at least two measures for the same individuals. "Correlations" are described in terms of a number, thus again providing much information in a very compact form. If a perfect positive relationship or agreement exists between two variables then the correlation coefficient (r) is +1.00. If no relationship exists it is 0.00. If the variables are totally independent of or in perfect disagreement with one another, then an inverse relationship exists and the r = −1.00. Intermediate values indicate trends, the strength of the trends depending upon the size of correlation. The basic formula for determining r requires us to divide the sum of all the deviations from the mean of both variables by the number of subjects and then to multiply by combined standard deviations. The formula looks like this:

$$r = \sqrt{\frac{[N\Sigma XY - (\Sigma X)(\Sigma Y)]^2}{[N\Sigma X^2 - (\Sigma X)^2][N\Sigma Y^2 - (\Sigma Y)^2]}}$$

Though there are less formidable looking formulas than this one, they all require the internal computations that are required above for the six values needed. The numbers do get cumbersome at times, though, so a pocket calculator is handy. Set up your data as shown in the following example, and the six values that you need are easily come by (N, ΣX, ΣX^2, ΣY, ΣY^2, and ΣXY).

X	Y	X^2	Y^2	X Y
10	4	100	16	40
12	8	144	64	96
15	10	225	100	150
21	15	441	225	315
8	6	64	36	48
3	1	9	1	3
14	6	196	36	84
16	12	256	144	192
18	10	324	100	180
8	4	64	16	32
$\Sigma X = 125$	$\Sigma Y = 76$	$\Sigma X^2 = 1,823$	$\Sigma Y^2 = 738$	$\Sigma XY = 1,140$

$N = 10$ (number of pairs of scores)

Note: An N of 10 is usually considered too small for use in calculating an r but for purposes of demonstration we can continue.

$$r = \sqrt{\frac{[N\Sigma XY - (\Sigma X)(\Sigma Y)]^2}{[N\Sigma X^2 - (\Sigma X)^2][N\Sigma Y^2 - (\Sigma Y)^2]}} = \sqrt{\frac{[10(1,140) - (125)(76)]^2}{[10(1,823) - (125)^2][10(738) - (76)^2]}}$$

$$= \sqrt{\frac{(11,400 - 9,500)^2}{(18,230 - 15,625)(7,380 - 5,776)}} = \sqrt{\frac{1,900^2}{(2,605)(1,604)}} = \sqrt{\frac{3,610,000}{4,178,420}}$$

$$r = \sqrt{.86}$$

$$r = .93$$

Since the correlation coefficient is perhaps one of the most valuable of all statistical tools yet at the same time is a most widely misused statistic, certain of its characteristics should be well understood. First of all a correlation coefficient regardless of its magnitude does not necessarily indicate a *causal* relationship. Even though a very high r is found between X and Y, for example, it may not be correctly inferred from this that X *causes* Y; the relationship between X and Y is merely stated by the correlation coefficient. An example of such an incorrect interpretation of r is this: thin girls wear small size dresses; therefore if one wears a small size dress this will cause one to be thin! Another point that should be noted is that the correlation coefficient does not represent a percentage of relationship. An r of .40 does not mean 40% agreement. Neither does an r of .40 imply twice the relationship of an r of .20, nor does an increase in r from .50 to .70 have the same meaning as an increase from .60 to .80. A correlation coefficient is just an index number. If the coefficient is squared, however, the resulting number may be interpreted as the percentage of variance accounted for by the relationship. In other words if r = .50 between X and Y then .25 or 25% ($.50^2$) of the variance due to chance is accounted for, but note that 75% of the time such a relationship between X and Y would be found by chance. A correlation must be high to be of significant predictive value but even modest correlations may reveal relationships of much importance. How high an r must be depends upon what we expect to do with it. Coefficients are interpreted in comparison with their standard errors. They are not absolute and they refer to the specific circumstances under which they were obtained; all statistics must be interpreted in terms of probable sampling errors. A rough interpretation of r is:

between 0 and .20—little or very little relationship

between .21 and .40—low relationship

between .41 and .60—some relationship but weak

between .61 and .80—high relationship

between .81 and 1.00—extremely high relationship

t TESTS

The t is the ratio of the difference between means and an indication of the variability of the sampling distribution. It tells us if there is a real difference between the mean scores of two variables or groups; that is, whether or not the magnitude of an observed difference is large enough to conclude that its occurrence should not be attributed to pure chance. Sometimes two groups are given different treatments and then compared on a criterion measure. Say, for example, we wish to know if the scores made by subjects who had distributed practice differed significantly from scores made by those subjects who had massed practice (in Experiment 4, "The Spacing of Practice"). Here the application of a t test would be appropriate. When experimental conditions are carefully controlled and only one variable is involved, a t test may then be applied to resulting data; the specific variable is then assumed to account for the difference observed between the scores, if that difference is sufficiently large.

Such tests are also used in hypothesis testing. By taking into consideration the ratio of differences between the means of the two groups and their standard deviations, a difference can be given quantitative value through use of the t test. The relationship obtained through use of such a formula is called a "critical ratio" and can be used to determine if the difference between the scores made by the two groups is large enough to show real (not chance) differences between the groups. Once these "critical ratios" or "t values" are known they can, by reference to appropriate tables, be interpreted to show how much confidence can be placed in them. If a t is found to be significant at the .01 or one per cent level of confidence, for example, then the obtained difference would be expected to occur by chance only once in one hundred times. If it is found that an event or circumstance might occur five times out of a hundred, then the investigator accepts, with lesser degree of confidence (.05 or five per cent), that this result is not due to pure chance.

Though the details for finding t are beyond the scope of this discussion, a simple example of the computation required follows:

Subject	Speed Test I	Speed Test II	Difference I-II	Deviation from mean of difference	Deviation squared
Dave	23	20	- 3	-1	+ 1
Jo	20	18	- 2	0	0
Phyl	19	15	- 4	-2	+ 4
Rose	18	14	- 4	-2	+ 4
M.L.	16	14	- 2	0	0
Dee	16	13	- 3	-1	+ 1
Tom	15	15	0	-2	+ 4
Deanie	15	13	- 2	0	0
Kathy	13	10	- 3	-1	+ 4
Kay	11	14	+ 3	-5	+25
George	10	8	- 2	0	0
Σ	176	154	-22		-40

Mean of Test I $\left(\dfrac{176}{11}\right) = 16$ Mean of Test II $\left(\dfrac{154}{11}\right) = 14$

Mean of difference $\left(\dfrac{-22}{11}\right) = -2$

Standard deviation of differences $\left(\sqrt{\dfrac{40}{10}}\right) = 2.0$

Standard error of difference $\left(\dfrac{2}{\sqrt{11}}\right) = .6$

$t\left(\dfrac{\text{Mean of difference}}{\text{Standard error of difference}}\right)$ or $\left(\dfrac{-2}{.6}\right) = -3.3$

$P < .01$

1

The Acquisition of Skill

What happens when we learn a new, complex motor activity? What happens before a well-skilled pattern emerges? High levels of achievement seldom result suddenly. Learning of this type usually involves a gradual process during which the learner progressively, though not always smoothly, approximates his goal. He gradually coordinates his actions, both temporal and spatial, during repeated practices. Practice gives him the opportunity to adapt his movements during many trials, in accordance with the nature of his errors and the quality of the available feedback (reinforcement).

Fitts[4] says that such learning moves through three stages: (1) the cognitive, (2) the fixation period, and (3) the autonomous stage. During initial learning certain knowledges and understandings of relationships must be developed and productive techniques and methods of moving are initiated. This is followed by more practice during which the learner attempts to improve and establish his manipulative abilities (make them more reliable and predictable). Finally the performer learns so well how to respond to external and internal cues that his movements require little conscious awareness.

In the present experiment, which is longer and more involved than any of the others described in this manual, you should observe behavioral changes associated with motor learning, and you should attempt to develop analytical insight regarding the integration of perceptual, proprioceptive and motor processes. Such integration is a requirement of motor proficiency. The present study should make clear to you also a very important point: the difference between the purpose and the problem of a study. Though the problem requires you to learn to juggle, to learn to do so is *not* the purpose of this experiment! The purpose is to critically examine the course of development of motor learning; the specific problem, which requires you to learn to juggle, is simply the example of motor learning which is to be used in attempting to achieve the purpose.

The assignment requires two types of data: (1) the objective evidence of learning as inferred from performance and (2) the recording of your subjective thoughts, plans, opinions and evaluations about the process of learning as you progress from the beginning to the more advanced stages of learning. The latter will give you subjective data but from this analytical approach you should gain insight into some problems of motor learning. You will be simultaneously the subject, the experimenter, and the recorder during this experiment. To be sure, this presents a limiting condition but experience has shown that this assignment can be accomplished in this manner. A short period of time on ten consecutive days is required for the accumulation of the necessary quantitative and qualitative data. This study is then to be written as though it were to be submitted for publication in either the *Research Quarterly* or the *Journal of Motor Behavior,* and is, therefore, the most important of the experiments.

PROBLEM

The problem is to critically examine the course of development of motor learning as it is exemplified in learning to juggle two tennis balls in one hand.

MATERIALS

Two tennis balls, paper, pencil, adequate space without a distracting background, good lighting, an interval timer or an alarm clock.

PROCEDURE

1. Attempt to juggle two tennis balls continuously in your preferred hand in a daily practice period of 5 minutes duration on each of 10 consecutive days. Throw one ball up and then the other, alternately throwing and catching, keeping the two balls in motion at once and under control.
2. At the end of each practice period record your frustrations, problems, pleasures, insights, and comments about methods tried, and the psychological aspects of performance which you experienced. Do not discuss this experiment with any of your classmates. Concentrate your thoughts on your own performance and learning process.

RESULTS

1. Count the number of successful catches you make during each trial and record the number. Juggle again and record catches, continuing until 5 minutes have elapsed. (Count "one" each time you catch a ball, so that your first day's record might look like this: 0-0-1-1-2-0-3-, etc.).
2. At the end of each five minute practice period record your observations and comments.
3. Count and record the total *number of trials* you made during the period (include zero scores as trials. They were!)
4. Add the *total number* of balls caught during the period.
5. Divide the total score by the total number of attempts (*average* score per trial).
6. Subtract your lowest daily score from your highest score (*range*).
7. Repeat each of the above steps for each practice period during the ten days.

DISCUSSION AND INFERENCES

Since your report is to be written in formal form, space is not provided here for answers to specific questions. Some are listed below, however, to help you begin to think about your data and how you will organize it.

1. What did you learn about learning a motor skill?
2. What factors seemed to increase your efficiency? decrease it?
3. What happened to *you* as you began to learn? to your *method*?
4. What happened to the number of trials per period as learning progressed? to the number of catches? to the range?
5. What occurred during the course of learning with reference to the size of movements? the space required? the energy required? the amount of tension? the quality of movement?
6. What relationships did you perceive regarding attitude, fatigue, confidence, emotions, motivations, performance?
7. If you wanted to record your typical daily performance what score would you use? Why not your best score?
8. What can you say about level of aspiration? the power of each trial in influencing the next?
9. Discuss your concept of the role of a teacher or coach.
10. Classify and give examples of feedback available in juggling and speculate on their importance relative to successful performance.

Table 1.1

Name of Subject _____		Date _____					
Trial	Score	Trial	Score	Trial	Score	Trial	Score
1		16		31		46	
2		17		32		47	
3		18		33		48	
4		19		34		49	
5		20		35		50	
6		21		36		51	
7		22		37		52	
8		23		38		53	
9		24		39		54	
10		25		40		55	
11		26		41		56	
12		27		42		57	
13		28		43		58	
14		29		44		59	
15		30		45		60	

Observations

Table 1.2

Name of Subject _____			Date _____				

Trial	Score	Trial	Score	Trial	Score	Trial	Score
1		16		31		46	
2		17		32		47	
3		18		33		48	
4		19		34		49	
5		20		35		50	
6		21		36		51	
7		22		37		52	
8		23		38		53	
9		24		39		54	
10		25		40		55	
11		26		41		56	
12		27		42		57	
13		28		43		58	
14		29		44		59	
15		30		45		60	

Observations

Table 1.3

| Name of Subject _____ Date _____ |

Trial	Score	Trial	Score	Trial	Score	Trial	Score
1		16		31		46	
2		17		32		47	
3		18		33		48	
4		19		34		49	
5		20		35		50	
6		21		36		51	
7		22		37		52	
8		23		38		53	
9		24		39		54	
10		25		40		55	
11		26		41		56	
12		27		42		57	
13		28		43		58	
14		29		44		59	
15		30		45		60	

Observations

Table 1.4

Name of Subject _____ . _____ Date _____							
Trial	Score	Trial	Score	Trial	Score	Trial	Score
1		16		31		46	
2		17		32		47	
3		18		33		48	
4		19		34		49	
5		20		35		50	
6		21		36		51	
7		22		37		52	
8		23		38		53	
9		24		39		54	
10		25		40		55	
11		26		41		56	
12		27		42		57	
13		28		43		58	
14		29		44		59	
15		30		45		60	

Observations

Table 1.5

Name of Subject _____				Date _____			
Trial	Score	Trial	Score	Trial	Score	Trial	Score
1		16		31		46	
2		17		32		47	
3		18		33		48	
4		19		34		49	
5		20		35		50	
6		21		36		51	
7		22		37		52	
8		23		38		53	
9		24		39		54	
10		25		40		55	
11		26		41		56	
12		27		42		57	
13		28		43		58	
14		29		44		59	
15		30		45		60	

Observations

Table 1.6

Name of Subject _____ Date _____

Trial	Score	Trial	Score	Trial	Score	Trial	Score
1		16		31		46	
2		17		32		47	
3		18		33		48	
4		19		34		49	
5		20		35		50	
6		21		36		51	
7		22		37		52	
8		23		38		53	
9		24		39		54	
10		25		40		55	
11		26		41		56	
12		27		42		57	
13		28		43		58	
14		29		44		59	
15		30		45		60	

Observations

Table 1.7

Name of Subject _____		Date _____	

Trial	Score	Trial	Score	Trial	Score	Trial	Score
1		16		31		46	
2		17		32		47	
3		18		33		48	
4		19		34		49	
5		20		35		50	
6		21		36		51	
7		22		37		52	
8		23		38		53	
9		24		39		54	
10		25		40		55	
11		26		41		56	
12		27		42		57	
13		28		43		58	
14		29		44		59	
15		30		45		60	

Observations

Table 1.8

| Name of Subject _____ Date _____ |

Trial	Score	Trial	Score	Trial	Score	Trial	Score
1		16		31		46	
2		17		32		47	
3		18		33		48	
4		19		34		49	
5		20		35		50	
6		21		36		51	
7		22		37		52	
8		23		38		53	
9		24		39		54	
10		25		40		55	
11		26		41		56	
12		27		42		57	
13		28		43		58	
14		29		44		59	
15		30		45		60	

Observations

Table 1.9

Name of Subject _____ Date _____

Trial	Score	Trial	Score	Trial	Score	Trial	Score
1		16		31		46	
2		17		32		47	
3		18		33		48	
4		19		34		49	
5		20		35		50	
6		21		36		51	
7		22		37		52	
8		23		38		53	
9		24		39		54	
10		25		40		55	
11		26		41		56	
12		27		42		57	
13		28		43		58	
14		29		44		59	
15		30		45		60	

Observations

Table 1.10

| Name of Subject _____ Date _____ |

Trial	Score	Trial	Score	Trial	Score	Trial	Score
1		16		31		46	
2		17		32		47	
3		18		33		48	
4		19		34		49	
5		20		35		50	
6		21		36		51	
7		22		37		52	
8		23		38		53	
9		24		39		54	
10		25		40		55	
11		26		41		56	
12		27		42		57	
13		28		43		58	
14		29		44		59	
15		30		45		60	

Observations

REFERENCES

1. Bilodeau, E.A. and Ina McD. Bilodeau, *Principles of Skill Acquisition,* New York: Academic Press, 1969.

2. ——, "Motor Skills Learning," *Annual Review of Psychology,* 12: 243-280, 1961.

3. Bryan, W.L. and Harter, N., "Studies on the Telegraphic Language: The Acquisition of a Hierarchy of Habits," *Psychological Review,* 6: 345-375, 1899.

4. Fitts, Paul M., and Posner, Michael I., *Human Performance* Belmont, California: Brooks/Cole Publishing Company, 1967 Chapter 2.

5. Knapp, Clyde G. and Dixon, Robert W., "Learning to Juggle: I. A Study to Determine the Effect of Two Different Distributions of Practice on Learning Efficiency," *Research Quarterly,* 21: 331-336, 1950.

6. ——, "Learning to Juggle: II. A Study of Whole and Part Methods," *Research Quarterly,* 23: 398-401, 1952.

7. Knapp, Clyde G., Dixon, Robert W., and Lazier, Murney, "Learning to Juggle: III. A Study of Performance by Two Different Age Groups," *Research Quarterly,* 29: 32-36, 1958.

2

The Relationship Between
Reaction Time and Movement Time

When a performance approaches excellence it is often attributed to the fact that the performer has "good reaction time." In many sports activities the "good" reaction time of the participant (often erroneously called "good reflexes") seemingly is a major component of high skill levels. Reaction time is defined as that lapse in time between the presentation of a stimulus and the first sign of overt response, this usually being a muscular response. It should be noted that this definition does not include that component of skill that is the speed of the movement itself. Reaction time then, is only a small part of the total time that any physical task requires for completion; and since it is determined by the response of neurophysiological mechanisms, it is usually considered to be somewhat predetermined, "set-in," or regulated more by genetic than environmental factors.

Movement time, on the other hand, is that amount of time from the first overt sign of movement to the completion of the task. Speed of movement, as suggested elsewhere in this manual, is highly specific varying from one part of the body to another as well as in the direction of movement. Movement time is also thought to vary with such factors as practice, strength, age, sex, joint mobility, and tissue consistency. Obviously both factors, i.e., reaction time and movement time, are important.

This experiment is designed to show the relationship between these two important components of skilled performance. As a result of this demonstration you should see whether or not a performer tends to be a "fast reactor" and a "fast mover" or if there seems to be no such predictable pattern.

PROBLEM

The problem is to compare two components of speed and determine, thereby, the relationship between reaction time and movement time.

MATERIALS

Photoelectric light source and relay,* two 100th second chronometers, proper electrical circuitry.

PROCEDURE

1. S is seated on a stool directly in front of the equipment with the reaction time button directly opposite the shoulder of his preferred hand.

2. S depresses reaction time button with the forefinger of his preferred hand with that finger pointing directly at the stimulus (a light). E gives command "Ready!" and within a one to four second time lapse, actuates the light.

---

*This device is described by Lois Youngen in "A Comparison of Reaction and Movement Time of Women Athletes and Non-Athletes," *Research Quarterly*, 30: 349-355, 1959, or see Appendix.

3. Upon seeing the light, S removes his finger from the reaction time button as quickly as possible and moves his hand as fast as possible through the photoelectric light beam (that is eleven inches away) with a "jabbing" movement.

4. Ten trials are given. The one to four second time lapse between the E's "ready" and the presentation of the light stimulus must be randomized among trials, else the S will learn to "jump the gun" successfully.

RESULTS

Record Reaction Time (x) and Movement Time (y) on Table 2.1. Using the formula, calculate r for these scores. (See Chapter "Basic Methods of Treating Data.")

Table 2.1

Name of Subject _____ Date _____

Trial	Reaction Time (X)	Movement Time (Y)	X²	Y²	XY
1	____	____	____	____	____
2	____	____	____	____	____
3	____	____	____	____	____
4	____	____	____	____	____
5	____	____	____	____	____
6	____	____	____	____	____
7	____	____	____	____	____
8	____	____	____	____	____
9	____	____	____	____	____
10	____	____	____	____	____
	$\Sigma X =$ ____	$\Sigma Y =$ ____	$\Sigma X^2 =$ ____	$\Sigma Y^2 =$ ____	$\Sigma XY =$ ____

$$r = \sqrt{\frac{[N\Sigma XY - (\Sigma X)(\Sigma Y)]^2}{[N\Sigma X^2 - (\Sigma X)^2][N\Sigma Y^2 - (\Sigma Y)^2]}}$$

$r =$

DISCUSSION AND INFERENCES

1. Using the data from the entire class, calculate r. What relationship exists between reaction time and movement time? What is the significance of this to the teacher of motor skills?

2. Is reaction time more highly related to speed in running the 100 yard dash or the 880? Elaborate on your answer.

3. Briefly list the physiological factors that are currently thought to increase or decrease reaction time.

4. Why is it an error to speak of "good reaction time" and "good reflexes" synonymously?

REFERENCES

1. Astrand, P.O., and Rodahl, Kaare, *Textbook of Work Physiology.* McGraw-Hill: New York, 1970.

2. Clarke, D.H., and Henry, Franklin, "Neuromotor Specificity and Increased Speed from Strength Development," *Research Quarterly,* 32: 315-325, 1961.

3. deVries, Herbert A., "The 'Looseness' Factor in Speed and O_2 Consumption of an Anaerobic 100-Yard Dash," *Research Quarterly,* 34: 305-313, 1963.

4. Ellis, Norman R., and Sloan, William, "Relationship Between Intelligence and Simple Reaction Time in Mental Defectives," *Perceptual and Motor Skills,* 8: 65-67, 1957.

5. Goodenough, Florence L., "The Development of the Reactive Process from Early Childhood to Maturity," *Journal of Experimental Psychology,* 18: 431-450, 1935.

6. McCloy, Charles H., "The Measurement of Speed in Motor Performance," *Psychometrika,* 5: 173-182, 1940.

3

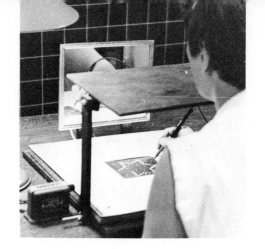

Bilateral Transfer of Learning

Experiments involving displaced vision have been widely used to investigate fundamental methods by which motor control is achieved, the genetic development of muscular coordination, adaptation in learning, bilateral transfer or "cross education," the effect of different intervals of practice upon the rate of improvement, interference, learning curves, and so on. This particular study involves observing the establishment of new coordination between motion and perception and utilizes one of the oldest and most used pieces of equipment which have been designed for the study of psychomotor learning. Mirror drawing apparatus requires movement which is not in agreement with your established habits. Note that the frequent change in direction of movement makes the task more difficult, requiring constant alertness and adjustment even though the equal length of the sections furnish regularity. Compare the effect of up-down and left-right relationships. The task is of sufficient length to be reasonably difficult and yet not cause undue fatigue. The present authors make no predictions, however, regarding your frustrations! The purpose of this experiment is both to demonstrate the phenomenon of bilateral transfer and to provide another example of the learning process.

PROBLEM

The problem is to determine the effect of unilateral practice on performance of the relatively unpracticed contralateral limb.

MATERIALS

Mirror tracing apparatus* seven star patterns for each subject, stop watch, sharp pencil.

PROCEDURE

1. Place a copy of the star pattern in the mirror tracing apparatus so that the arrow points to the upper right corner of the paper. It should be placed directly in front of the subject.

2. S sits comfortably in front of the apparatus and adjusts the shield so that the star pattern is visible to him only indirectly by looking into the upright mirror.

3. Using a sharp pencil, S traces the outline with his *non-preferred hand*, starting on the arrow and moving in the direction indicated. S should try not to touch or cross the lines bordering the pathway. He must keep his pencil in contact with the paper. He must not lift his pencil from the

---

*The "homemade" star tracing apparatus illustrated above, designed by Robert Sorani, uses electrical circuitry to count errors. The experiment described here is done without such circuitry; errors are simply counted "by hand." Commercial models are available, both of the traditional and electrical type.

paper. Should he move outside the border of the star he should draw a line back as near as possible to the point of error, and continue.

4. S traces five more patterns with his *preferred hand* using the star pattern provided. E assures that the patterns are marked in proper sequence.

5. S traces one more pattern with his *non-preferred hand.*

6. Provide a 30 second rest period between all trials.

7. Time the performance.

RESULTS

Count the number of times the tracing line touches or goes outside the lines of the star. Record these errors on Table 5.1. Also note and record the elapsed time in seconds for completion of each trial. Compute your score for each trial by the following formula:

$$\text{Score} = \frac{100}{\text{seconds} + \text{errors.}}$$

Table 3.1

Name of Subject: _____ Date: _____			

Errors:	Time in Seconds:	Score:
Trial 1 _____ Non-preferred hand	_____	_____
Trial 2 _____ Preferred hand	_____	_____
Trial 3 _____ Preferred hand	_____	_____
Trial 4 _____ Preferred hand	_____	_____
Trial 5 _____ Preferred hand	_____	_____
Trial 6 _____ Preferred hand	_____	_____
Trial 7 _____ Non-preferred hand	_____	_____

Find per cent improvement for non-preferred hand:

$$\frac{\text{Trial 7 Score}}{\text{Trial 1 Score}} = \% \text{ Improvement}$$

TRIAL 1. NON-PREFERRED HAND

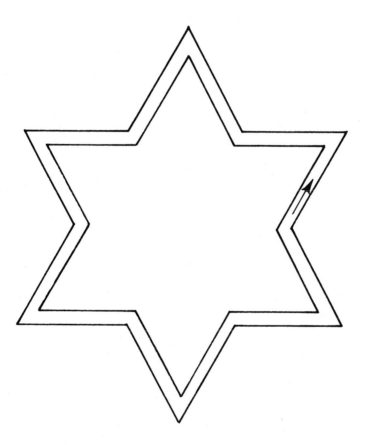

Name _____   Number of errors _____

Date _____   Elapsed time _____

TRIAL 2. PREFERRED HAND

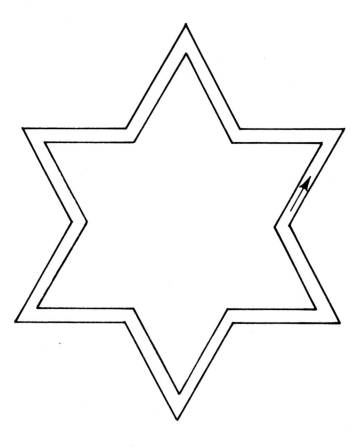

Name _____ Number of errors _____

Date _____ Elapsed time _____

TRIAL 3. PREFERRED HAND

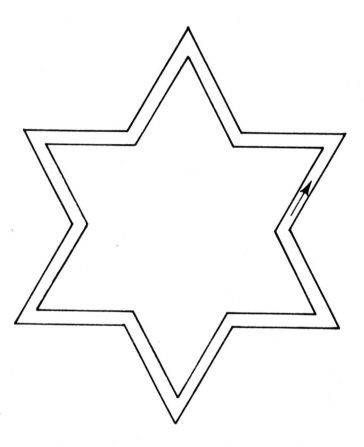

me _____   Number of errors _____

te _____   Elapsed time _____

TRIAL 4. PREFERRED HAND

Name _____   Number of errors _____

Date _____   Elapsed time _____

TRIAL 5. PREFERRED HAND

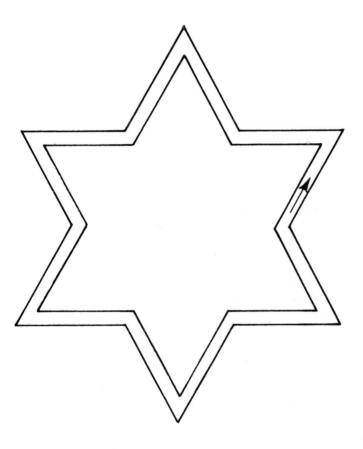

Name _____ Number of errors _____

Date _____ Elapsed time _____

TRIAL 6. PREFERRED HAND

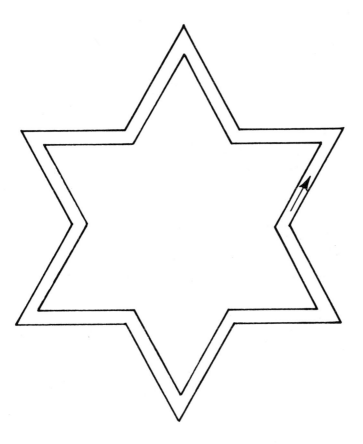

Name _____   Number of errors _____

Date _____   Elapsed time _____

TRIAL 7. NON-PREFERRED HAND

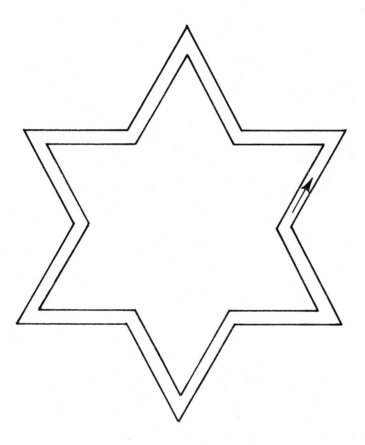

Name _____   Number of errors _____

Date _____   Elapsed time _____

DISCUSSION AND INFERENCES

1. Describe subjectively the course of learning evidenced during the five trials with the preferred hand.

2. We all are familiar with the displacement of vision that occurs when looking in a mirror. It occurs when a man shaves, or ties his tie, when a woman combs her hair or puts on makeup. With this much practice at this type of task, how do you explain the difficulty usually encountered in this experiment?

3. Why was the second performance with the non-preferred, non-practiced hand improved? What is this phenomenon called? Do you know any other name for it?

4. How can you account for the improvement probably exhibited during the last trial with the non-preferred hand? Would you expect the magnitude of the bilateral effect ever to exceed that of direct practice?

5. You will note that in this experiment we have referred to the "preferred" and the "non-preferred hand," not the "dominant" and the "non-dominant." Can you suggest why the former is preferable?

REFERENCES

1. Buchwald, Jennifer, "Proprioceptive Reflexes and Posture," *American Journal of Physical Medicine,* 46: 1-4-113, 1967.

2. Cook, T.W. "Studies in Cross Education: I—Mirror Tracing in the Star-Shaped Maze," *Journal of Experimental Psychology,* 16: 144-160, 1933; "II—Further Experiments in Mirror Tracing the Star-Shaped Maze," 16: 679-700, 1933; "III—Kinesthetic Learning of an Irregular Pattern," 17: 749-762, 1934; "IV—Permanence of Transfer," 18: 255-266, 1935.

3. Hellebrandt, F.A., "Cross Education: Ipsilateral and Contralateral Effects of Unimanual Training," *Journal of Applied Physiology,* 4: 136-144, 1951.

4. Hellebrandt, F.A., Parrish, Annie M., and Houtz, Sara Jane, "Cross Education: The Influences of Unilateral Exercise on the Contralateral Limb," *Archives of Physical Medicine,* 28: 76-84, 1947.

5. Loofbourrow, G.N., "Neuromuscular Integration," in *Science and Medicine of Exercise and Sports,* Warren R. Johnson, (ed). New York: Harper and Brothers, 1960.

6. Scripture, E.W., "Cross Education," *Appleton's Popular Science Monthly,* 56: 589-596, March, 1900.

7. Wissler, Clark, and Richardson, W.W., "Diffusion of the Motor Impulse," *Psychological Review,* 7: 29-38, 1900.

4

The Spacing of Practice

Massed versus Distributed

Under what conditions should a task be practiced? Is it better to concentrate practice into longer but fewer periods or to distribute it into shorter but more practice periods? As early as 1885 Ebbinghaus found that spaced practice was more effective than massed practice when learning such things as lists of nonsense syllables or numbers. The results of more recent studies involving the learning of motor tasks have generally agreed with those early findings; however, the best arrangement of practice time is not only concerned with the length and frequency of practice periods but also is related to such factors as the complexity and demands of the task, the age and physical state of the learner, the motivational and aspirational level of the learner, the stage to which the learning has progressed (*i.e.*, beginning, intermediate, advanced), and the meaningfulness of the task to the learner. As a result it is impossible to determine a one best schedule for practice. Nevertheless distributed practice has been found almost universally to be superior to massed practice during the early learning of motor activities.

The labyrinthian maze is a task unfamiliar to most persons, but it may have some degree of familiarity to some subjects. The object of the task is to steer a steel ball through a series of cul de sacs and proper passageways from the beginning to the end of the maze by manipulating two knobs that control the angles of slant of the platform upon which the maze is constructed. The purpose of this experiment is to make observations concerning the scheduling of practices upon naive, not-so-naive, and well-skilled performers.

PROBLEM

The problem is to compare the effects of massed and distributed practice while performing, at various levels of ability, the labyrinthian maze.

MATERIALS

Labyrinthian maze*, stop watch, suitable table and chairs, hand counter.

PROCEDURE

1. This experiment should be done during a laboratory session (preferably the first) when all class members are present and can establish a criterion score as follows: Each S (all class members) positions himself comfortably with the maze on a table in front of him. Each is administered a one-minute trial by E and the subject's three single highest scores are averaged and recorded.

---

*May be purchased commercially from almost any toy store.

2. Each S then finds a partner whose criteria score (from # 1) is as close as possible to his own.

3. One partner then practices on the maze for a continuous four minute period of time. The other partner practices for twelve 20-second trials with 10 second rest between each trial. Record the results of all trials and find a mean (average) score for the best 50% of the trials of each S.

RESULTS

Record the score for each trial for the criterion trial. Using the mean of the best three trials, record a criterion score.

Record score and the mean of the top 50% of the score for each S.

Table 4.1

Name of Subject _____

Scores on criterion trial _____

Total of top three scores: _____

Average (Criterion Score): _____

Name of Subject's Partner_____

Criterion score of partner_____

Scores on massed or distributed practice trims:

Total of best 50%_____

Mean of best 50%_____

Partner's mean of best 50%_____

DISCUSSION AND INFERENCES

1. Which method produced the better performance? Are your results consistent with those found in current research dealing with this subject?

2. In some elementary schools, physical education periods are scheduled only once per week. Comment on this as good educational practice.

3. If each of you continued practice daily until a certain criterion score was reached, how do you think learning curves resulting from massed and distributed practice methods might differ on this task? Illustrate your answer with a rough graph.

4. How should the length of practices and their spacing be different for beginning physical education classes as compared to varsity athletics?

REFERENCES

1. Ebbinghaus, Hermann, *Memory* (the 1885 publication translated from the German in 1913 by H.A. Ruger and C.E. Bussenius and now available in paperback as *Memory: A Contribution to Experimental Psychology*). New York: Dover Publications Inc., 1964.

2. Richardson, J.R., Chang, G.X., and Harding, J.P., "Effect of the Amount of Practice Type of Instruction and Secondary Task Load on the Learning of a Large Muscle Skill." in *Proceedings of the Fourth Canadian Symposium on Psycho-Motor Learning and Sports Psychology,* Williams, Jan D. and Leonard M. Wankel, (eds.) Ottawa: Department of National Health and Welfare, 1973.

3. Singer, Robert, "Massed and Distributed Practice Effects on the Acquisition and Retention of a Novel Basketball Skill," *Research Quarterly,* 36: 68-77, 1965.

4. Travis, Roland C., "Practice and Rest Periods in Motor Learning," *Journal of Psychology* 3: 183-189, 1937.

5. Waglow, I.F., "Effect of School Term Length on Skill Achievement in Tennis, Golf and Handball," *Research Quarterly,* 37: 157-159, 1966.

6. Woodworth, Robert S., and Schlosberg, Harold, *Experimental Psychology*. New York: Holt, Rinehart, and Winston, 1965. (See section on "Massed vs. Spaced Learning," 786-794).

5

Retroactive Interference in Learning

Anything that conflicts, hinders or is incompatible with that to be learned causes interference or inhibition. Retroactive describes the direction of the interference: backward. When the effects of backward action are negative, the phenomenon is called retroactive interference or retroactive inhibition. The way retroactive interference is customarily demonstrated and measured is by (1) learning task A, (2) learning task B (interpolated), then (3) repeating task A. In this way the effect of the interpolated activity B on the original task A can be determined. After the activity is interpolated if performance of A is worsened then interference or inhibition caused by task B is presumed to account for the result. It is known that certain variables are related to the amount of interference: the relative similarity of A and B, the extent of proficiency achieved in A and B, the timing of the tasks, et cetera. An often used task, simple though frustrating, by which to demonstrate interference is card sorting.

PROBLEM

The problem of this experiment is to determine the effects of retroactive interference on learning.

MATERIALS

Card sorting box*, two decks** of Flinch cards, stop watch.

PROCEDURE

(Each S should allow enough time to complete number one through five *without interruption*)

1. E shuffles one deck of cards five times.

2. S sits in front of the card sorting box, the various compartments of which are numbered in random fashion.

3. E instructs S, "On the signal, 'Ready? Go!' hold one deck of cards face up (numbers visible) and sort them into the proper compartments as fast as possible. Do not attempt to correct any errors you may make."

4. E uses the stop watch to measure the elapsed time for each of five trials. During the trials the second deck of cards should be shuffled by E thus readying them for the subsequent trial.

---

*This device consists of a wooden bottomless box 15 1/2 inches deep by 19 inches across, divided on the inside into 15 equal sections which are numbered in random order 1-15. It must be possible to alter the randomization. In the above homemade device this is accomplished by reversing the small strips of wood on which the numbers appear. Card sorting boxes may be purchased commercially.
**To easily distinguish one deck of cards from the other, mark one edge of one of the decks with a wide felt marker.

5. Thirty seconds rest should be allowed between each trial. During this time E lifts the card sorter and determines the number of errors made by S.

6. E turns numbered strips on the card sorter over to reveal a new random numbering arrangement for each compartment. The above procedure is repeated five times thus providing practice on the new (interpolated) arrangement of numbers.

7. E returns compartment numbers to original order and allows S two more trials on the original task.

RESULTS

Record the elapsed time for each trial and total these. Record numbers of errors for each trial in a similar manner.

SCORING

$$\frac{\text{Total number of errors} + \text{total elapsed time (in seconds)}}{1{,}000}$$

Table 5.1

Name of Subject: _____ Date: _____

First random arrangement of numbers:

Number of Errors: Elapsed Time:

Trial 1 _____   _____

Trial 2 _____   _____

Trial 3 _____   _____

Trial 4 _____   _____

Trial 5 _____   _____

Total: _____   _____

Score: _____

Second random arrangement of numbers:

Number of Errors: Elapsed Time:

Trial 1 _____   _____

Trial 2 _____   _____

Trial 3 _____   _____

Trial 4 _____   _____

Trial 5 _____   _____

Total: _____   _____

Score: _____

Repeat of first random arrangement of numbers:

Number of Errors: Elapsed Time:

Trial 1 _____   _____

Trial 2 _____   _____

Total: _____   _____

Score: _____

DISCUSSION AND INFERENCES

1. Do you believe that ability acquired during the first five trials is destroyed by the rearrangement or just "laid aside?" Support your answer.

2. What implications regarding dance or aquatics are suggested by this demonstration?

3. List physical education skills which you believe should not be taught together because of possible interference.

4. Coaches and highly skilled performers often make such statements as, "If you are a trackman, don't swim." Is this good advice?

REFERENCES

1. Gentile, A.M., "A Working Model of Skill Acquisition with Application to Teaching" *Quest XVII* January, 1972 pp. 3-23.

2. Lewis, D.P., Smith, N., and McAllister, D.E., "Retroactive Facilitation and Interference in Perform ance on the Modified Two-hand Coordinator," *Journal of Experimental Psychology,* 44: 44-50, 1952.

3. McGeoch, J.A., and McDonald, W.T., "Meaningful Relation and Retroactive Inhibition," *American Journal of Psychology,* 43: 579-588, 1931.

4. Melton, A.W., and van Lackum, W.J., "Retroactive and Proactive Inhibition: Evidence for a Two factor Theory of Retroactive Inhibition," *American Journal of Psychology,* 54: 157-173, 1941.

5. Oxendine, Joseph B., *Psychology of Motor Learning.* New York: Appleton-Century-Crofts, 1968.

6

Retention of Learning

That which is meaningful and useful we are most likely to remember. The type of task and the degree of its organization are factors which affect retention. The degree of original learning also affects retention, and this is at least partially a function of overlearning. Overlearning by definition means practice carried on beyond some established criterion; it is assumed that the additional practice is responsible for increased strength and depth of learning and that these conditions enhance memory. Within certain limits, the more a task is overlearned, the greater its retention, the higher the accuracy and speed with which it can be performed after lay-off, and the shorter the amount of time necessary to return to the level of proficiency originally attained.

The pursuit of a target on a circular path (the pursuit rotor) is a classical demonstration, having been used for years in the study of almost all of the important problems of learning: warm-up effect, learning decrement, massed and distributed practice, whole and part learning, retention, reminiscence, reinforcement, interference, and transfer. The subject's task is to attempt to keep a loosely hinged stylus in contact with a small rotating disk, a perfect score being 100 per cent on target. This task requires precision, coordination, and finely timed movement. The purpose of the present experiment is to demonstrate retention of learning.

PROBLEM

The problem is to determine the effects of different amounts of practice on the retention of these tasks as indicated by performance.

MATERIALS

Pursuit rotor*, non-pressure stylus, chronometer, proper electrical circuitry, suitable table and chair.

PROCEDURE

1. Work in groups of four persons.
2. E sets the pursuit rotor at sixty revolutions per minute.
3. S sits comfortably (at a suitable height) beside the pursuit rotor holding the stylus in his preferred hand. The stylus has a spring-type hinge and the S's *hand or fingers must not touch, be on, or over the hinge.*

Chronometer

---

*Though pursuit rotors are commercially available, a very usable substitute can be inexpensively built from a phonograph turntable that is wired to a 100th second chronometer. See Appendix.

4. At the signal, "Ready? Go!" E starts the pursuit rotor and S_1 attempts to keep the stylus on the target.

5. Five 20-second practice trials are given with a 10-second rest period between each trial. Record the time on target for each trial.

6. S_2, S_3, and S_4 repeat above except that these subjects are given 10, 15, and 20 20-second trials respectively.

7. Calculate and record the mean scores for each subject. (Divide each S's total score by the number of trials allowed.)

8. After one week of no practice, each S repeats three additional 20-second trials. Calculate and record the per cent of retention of mean time for each subject as explained in reference number five.

RESULTS

Calculate, record, and compare per cent of retention scores between S differences.

DISCUSSION AND INFERENCES

1. Distinguish between overlearning and overloading. In what kinds of motor tasks and for what purposes are each advised?

2. Was any relationship found between the amount of practice time allowed and the amount of retention observed?

3. In relation to per cent of retention, what does the term "savings" mean?

4. Just what do you think is retained—technique? Skill? Understanding? Make one application of your answer to teaching or coaching motor activities.

REFERENCES

1. Fleishman, Edwin, and Parker, James, "Factors in the Retention and Relearning of Perceptual–Motor Skill," *Journal of Experimental Psychology,* 64: 215-226, 1962.

2. Luh, C.W., "The Conditions of Retention," *Psychological Monographs,* No. 142, 1922.

3. McGeoch, John, *The Psychology of Human Learning.* New York: David McKay Co., 1961.

4. Miller, Donna Mae, *Coaching the Female Athlete,* Philadelphia: Lea and Febiger, 1974 "Staleness," pp. 149-150.

5. Purdy, Bonnie J., and Lockhart, Aileene, "Retention and Relearning of Gross Motor Skills After Long Periods of No Practice," *Research Quarterly,* 33: 265-272, 1962.

Table 6.1 Time on Target (1st Practice)

S_1	S_2	S_3	S_4
Trial 1 _____	1 _____	1 _____	1 _____
2 _____	2 _____	2 _____	2 _____
3 _____	3 _____	3 _____	3 _____
4 _____	4 _____	4 _____	4 _____
5 _____	5 _____	5 _____	5 _____
	6 _____	6 _____	6 _____
Mean ═════	7 _____	7 _____	7 _____
	8 _____	8 _____	8 _____
	9 _____	9 _____	9 _____
	10 _____	10 _____	10 _____
		11 _____	11 _____
	Mean ═════	12 _____	12 _____
		13 _____	13 _____
		14 _____	14 _____
		15 _____	15 _____
		Mean ═════	16 _____
			17 _____
			18 _____
			19 _____
			20 _____
			Mean ═════

Table 6.2 Time on Target (2nd Practice)

	S_1	S_2	S_3	S_4
Trial 1	_____	_____	_____	_____
2	_____	_____	_____	_____
3	_____	_____	_____	_____
Totals:	_____	_____	_____	_____
Mean:	_____	_____	_____	_____
% Retention:	_____	_____	_____	_____

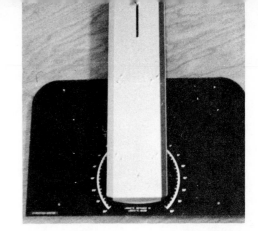

The Effect of Knowledge of Results on Performance

Although practice is a necessary requirement for improvement, mere repetition will not necessarily result in increased proficiency. The performer needs knowledge of results so he will have the information which is necessary to improve his performance and so he can maintain his desire to do so. KOR comes from the feedback which is gained by comparing one's performance with some standard of achievement (extrinsic or external feedback, often called "augmented"), and from the sensations or cues which result from and accompany performance (intrinsic or internal feedback).

In many activities it is possible to know almost immediately after performance how one has performed quantitatively. Evaluation may be made with reference to error (placement on a target such as in archery or bowling), or with reference to speed (time of completing the gates on a downhill ski race). Evaluation is more difficult when judgment is made qualitatively (the "goodness" of a gymnastic move). One can often also sense whether movement has or has not been effective—it "feels right" (the basketball player knows the ball will enter the basket as soon as it leaves his hands; the bowler knows he has rolled a strike). It is hoped that through the investigation described below the need for some kind of KOR will be demonstrated to you.

PROBLEM

The problem is to compare performance when KOR is withheld with performance which is accompanied with one type of verbal cue.

MATERIALS

Kinesthesiometer,* blindfold.

PROCEDURE

1. S is blindfolded, then seated at a table with the kinesthesiometer directly in front of him, the chair being at such a height that when the S moves the apparatus, the only movement of his arm is medial rotation. The angle of arm flexion should remain the same throughout the experiment.

2. The elbow of S should touch the lip of the tray and S should adjust the knob at the far end so it rests comfortably between his first and second fingers.

3. The apparatus should be placed so that the S's arm is directly in the sagittal plane. S is told that his arm is now at zero degrees.

---

*This apparatus is commercially available. The experiment may also be done by substituting a large protractor drawn on paper or on a table. The radius should be sixteen to twenty inches long in order to accommodate forearms of various lengths.

4. E arbitrarily chooses and records seven points on the quadrant ranging from 1 degree to 90 degrees
   E then instructs S to move to each of the seven ranges he has chosen. (Do not present these in exac
   ascending or descending order of magnitude; use a random order.) Between each positioning, S'
   arm is returned to zero degrees. Give S no knowledge of results.

5. Repeat procedures one through four above but this time E appraises S of the amount of error afte
   each movement is made. For example, E may ask S to move to 43 degrees. S moves to 47 degrees. I
   says to S, "You have moved to 47 degrees, 4 degrees too far." After returning S's arm to zero, I
   then asks S to move to the next chosen point and notifies S of any error made there.

RESULTS

Calculate total positive errors in degrees (when S went beyond criterion) and total negative errors ir
degrees (when S fell short of the criterion). Record these errors on the charts as indicated with and
without KOR.

DISCUSSION AND INFERENCES

1. When KOR was withheld was the S consistently an "undershooter" or "overshooter?" Did KOR
   alter this tendency?

2. Are you able to conclude, on the basis of the data collected during the first half of this study
   (results of trials without verbal cues), that kinesthetic perception can be improved with practice
   alone? How was performance affected when KOR was given?

Table 7.1 (Without KOR)

Name of Subject _____ Date _____

Degrees
Chosen   Number of degrees in error + or −

1 _____   Trial 1 _____

2 _____   2 _____

3 _____   3 _____

4 _____   4 _____

5 _____   5 _____

6 _____   6 _____

7 _____   7 _____

                                           Total positive error: _____

                                           Total negative error: _____

                    Considering all numbers as positive: Average error:_____

Table 7.2 (With KOR)

Name of Subject _____ Date _____

Degrees
Chosen   Number of degrees in error + or −

1 _____   Trial 1 _____

2 _____   2 _____

3 _____   3 _____

4 _____   4 _____

5 _____   5 _____

6 _____   6 _____

7 _____   7 _____

                                           Total positive error:_____

                                           Total negative error: _____

                    Considering all numbers as positive: Average error:_____

3. What implications regarding the importance of KOR can be made toward teaching such things as the golf swing where the movement pattern is generally considered more important (in early learning) than the results, i.e., where and how far the ball goes?

4. Considering the kind and intensity of feedback which occur, speculate on the value of manual guidance as compared with auditory and visual ones.

REFERENCES

1. Annett, J., and Kay, H., "Knowledge of Results and Skilled Performance," *Occupational Psychology,* 31: 69-79, 1957.

2. Fitts, Paul M., "Perceptual-Motor Skill Learning," 244-293, in A.W. Melton (ed.) *Categories of Human Learning.* New York: Academic Press, 1964.

3. Henry, Franklin, "Dynamic Kinesthetic Perception and Adjustment," *Research Quarterly,* 24: 176, 1953.

4. Holding, D.H., *Principles of Training.* New York: Pergamon Press, 1965.

5. Leuba, J.H., "The Influence of the Duration and of the Rate of Arm Movements Upon the Judgment of Their Length," *American Journal of Psychology,* 20: 374-385, 1909.

6. Philips, M., and Summers, D., "Relation of Kinesthetic Perception to Motor Learning," *Research Quarterly,* 25: 456-469, 1954.

7. Robb, Margaret, "Feedback," *Quest,* (Symposium on Motor Learning), 6: 38-43, 1966.

8

Augmented Knowledge of Results

It is thought that no learning is possible without feedback or knowledge of results. It has also been suggested that when KOR is augmented by use of more than one sensory modality, learning may be enhanced.

PROBLEM

The problem is to determine the effect of augmenting KOR with an auditory signal while learning the maze.

MATERIALS

Maze, stop watch, stylus, buzzer, proper electrica 1 circuitry.

PROCEDURE

1. Work in groups of three (2S, 1E). Cover the maze from the view of both S. E will not become an S in this experiment. S is blindfolded.

2. S_1 will be timed for five trips through the maze. Allow a rest between trials. During these trials the buzzer is *not* connected.

3. S_2 repeats as in #2 above except that the buzzer is connected and a buzz is heard when cul de sacs are entered. Allow a rest between trials.

RESULTS

Post and obtain results from all S_1 and S_2 in the entire class and record on the next page.

DISCUSSION AND INFERENCES

1. Just "eyeballing" the data, what conclusions can you draw?

Table 8.1

Total Time for Each S_1 in Class	Total Time for Each S_2 in Class
Trial 1 _____	Trial 1 _____
Trial 2 _____	Trial 2 _____
Trial 3 _____	Trial 3 _____
Trial 4 _____	Trial 4 _____
Trial 5 _____	Trial 5 _____
Mean Time S_1 _____	Mean Time S_2 _____

2. Why should augmented KOR affect learning?

3. Can you give examples in other motor activity learning situations where this phenomenon could enhance learning?

4. Which sensory modalities are most important in the performance of motor activities?

REFERENCES

1. Adams, Jack, Goetz, Ernest, and Phillips, H. Marshall. "Response Feedback and Motor Learning." *Journal of Experimental Psychology* 92: 391-397, 1972.

2. Arnett, John. *Feedback and Human Behavior.* Baltimore: Penguin Books, 1969.

3. Gordon, Norman B. "Guidance versus Augmented Feedback and Motor Skill: *Journal of Experimental Psychology,* 77: 24-30, 1968.

4. Heimstra, Norman W., and Vernon S. Ellingstad. Human Behavior: *A Systems Approach,* Monterey, California: Brooks/Cole, 1972.

9

Positive Transfer of Learning

Positive transfer or proactive facilitation is said to occur when previous experience aids in the learning or performance of a subsequent task. If a prior task interferes or conflicts with the new task, this is termed negative transfer or proactive interference. (Of course this situation can be reversed; the second task may retroactively also affect the original task, either positively or negatively). If one task has no effect on another then no transfer has occurred.

The possibility that attitudes, knowledges and understandings can transfer from one situation to another is basic to all formal education. The chances that positive transfer may occur are enhanced if movements employed in the first task are used in the second, if the performer perceives a principle which applies to both circumstances, and if he sees that generalizations or insights developed in one situation are appropriate to another. The purpose here is to demonstrate the phenomenon of positive transfer.

PROBLEM

The problem of this experiment is to determine the effect of prior experience on the performance of a new task.

MATERIALS

Mirror tracing apparatus, one star pattern per S, five new target patterns per S, sharp pencil.

PROCEDURE

1. S *must* previously and at another time have completed Experiment 3 on bilateral transfer of learning. Do not proceed unless this has been done.

2. S sits in front of the mirror tracing apparatus. E places the star pattern so that it is obscured by the screen. S must be able to see the star only by looking in the mirror.

3. S traces the star with his preferred hand, moving in the direction indicated by the arrow. One trial is given. S thus reviews his prior learning from the experiment on bilateral transfer, previously completed.

4. E then replaces the star with a copy of the new target. Using a sharp pencil, S traces the outline with his preferred hand, starting on the arrow and moving in the direction indicated. S should try not to touch or cross the lines bordering the pathway. He must keep his pencil in contact with the paper, never lifting it from the paper. If he should move outside the border of the pathway he should draw a line back as near as possible to the point of error, and continue.

5. This is repeated until five trials have been completed using the patterns provided.

6. Provide a 30 second rest period between all trials.

RESULTS

Count the number of times that the S touched or went outside the pathway of the pattern on each of the five trials. Record the total of these scores on Table 6.1. Also record the time in seconds which was required to complete each trial. Compute the score for each trial by the following formula:

$$Score = \frac{100}{seconds \ plus \ errors}$$

Table 9.1

Name of Subject _____ Date _____		
Errors	Time	Score
Trial 1 _____	_____	_____
Trial 2 _____	_____	_____
Trial 3 _____	_____	_____
Trial 4 _____	_____	_____
Trial 5 _____	_____	_____

Practice and Review for Experiment 9: Positive Transfer of Learning

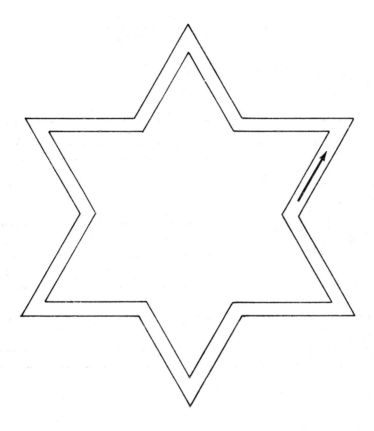

Elapsed Time _____ Name _____

Number of Errors _____ Date _____

TRIAL 1. POSITIVE TRANSFER OF LEARNING

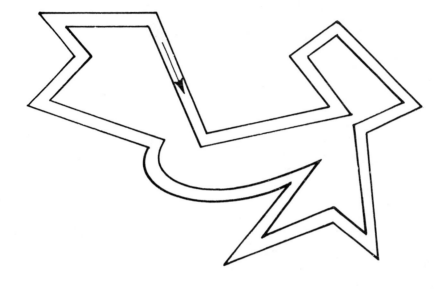

Name _____   Trial No. _____

Date _____   Score _____

Elapsed Time _____

Number of Errors _____

TRIAL 2. POSITIVE TRANSFER OF LEARNING

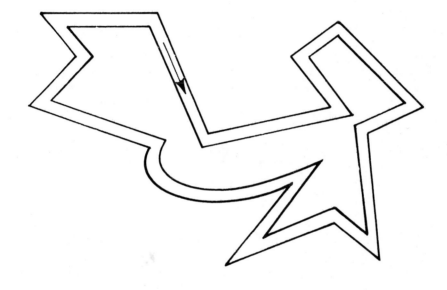

Name _____ Trial No. _____

Date _____ Score _____

Elapsed Time _____

Number of Errors _____

TRIAL 3. POSITIVE TRANSFER OF LEARNING

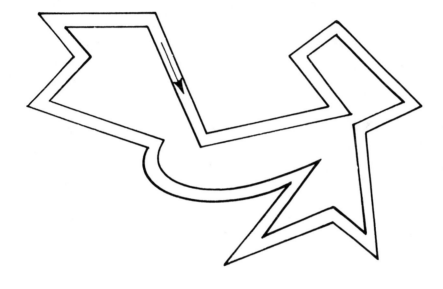

Name _____   Trial No. _____

Date _____   Score _____

Elapsed Time _____

Number of Errors _____

TRIAL 4. POSITIVE TRANSFER OF LEARNING

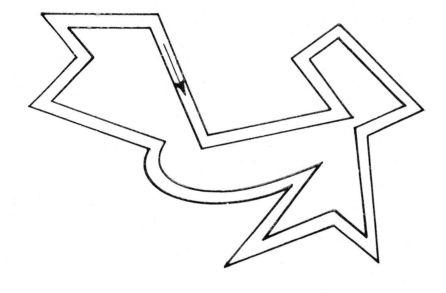

Name _____   Trial No. _____

Date _____   Score _____

Elapsed Time _____

Number of Errors _____

TRIAL 5. POSITIVE TRANSFER OF LEARNING

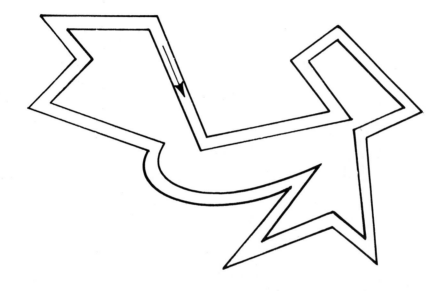

Name _____ Trial No. _____

Date _____ Score _____

Elapsed Time _____

Number of Errors _____

DISCUSSION AND INFERENCES

1. Compare your data, Experiments 3 and 9. Which task was learned more rapidly, the star or the new pattern? Can you explain these results?

2. Compare the kind of errors you made during the learning of the two different tasks.

3. Could the learning of the two tasks have been reversed (the new targets practiced first) and still demonstrate the phenomenon?

4. Would you expect positive transfer to occur between such tasks as the baseball swing and the golf swing? The overhead smashes in tennis and badminton? A good sprint start and the offensive lineman's charge? The hockey and golf drives?

REFERENCES

1. Drowatzky, John N. *Motor Learning Principles and Practices* Minneapolis: Burgess, 1975. Chapter 5 "Transfer."

2. Gagné, Robert M., and Fleishman, Edwin, *Psychology and Human Performance.* New York: Holt Rinehart and Winston, 1959. ("Transfer of Training in Motor Skills," 251-260).

3. Johnston, William A., "Transfer of Team Skills as a Function of Type of Training," *Journal o Applied Psychology* 50: 102-108, 1966.

4. Nelson, Dale O., "Studies of Transfer of Learning in Gross Motor Skills, *Research Quarterly* 28: 364-373, 1957.

5. Webb, L.W., "Transfer of Training and Retroaction, a Comparative Study," *Psychological Mono graphs,* Number 104, 1917.

10

Perception of Force

To be able to reproduce movement and to make quick adjustments requires information that is made available both by the exteroceptors (pressure and touch) and proprioceptors (movement at joints). To be able to impart force appropriately and consistently is essential to success in certain sports. The short serve in badminton requires a relatively small amount of force but unless it is consistently imparted the serve will be unsuccessful. Medium force must be used when attempting a basketball free throw. The pressure in this case by the opposing guard has been eliminated, but a real problem remains, that of reproducing force and trajectory under circumstances which impose a different kind of pressure.

Some persons seem to be consistently inconsistent, no matter the task; they undershoot one moment and overshoot the next with no detectable pattern in their inconsistencies. On the other hand, some persons appear to impart too much force, consistently overshooting through the entire range, while others tend to be consistent "undershooters." Many have developed great specific reliabilities; they can be counted on in specific circumstances. The problem of perceiving and producing just the right amount of force is a subtle but imperative aspect of successful performance; it is the subject of this experiment.

PROBLEM

The problem is to determine your ability to perceive and reproduce force.

MATERIALS

Hand dynamometer.

PROCEDURE

1. Examine the dynamometer, experiment with it and learn to read it before starting the experiment. Hold it in the palm of the preferred hand with the dial facing the palm so that the fingers or body will not interfere with the dial.

2. E asks S to squeeze the dynamometer as hard as possible. Then E requests that S "squeeze it lightly" and then "about half as hard as possible." Record the results of these three "standard" efforts.

3. E then mixes up nine commands, three for each "standard" force. (E asks S to repeat maximum force three times, "half" force three times, and "light" force three times, but these should not be presented in any patterned order).

4. Allow sufficient rest between trials. The S is not apprised of the results of trials.

5. Repeat with non-preferred hand.

RESULTS

Record the three standard forces and then the scores of the nine randomized trials for maximum, half, and light forces. Note magnitude and direction of errors.

Table 10.1

Name _____	Date _____

Standard forces exerted: Preferred hand

Maximum _____

Half _____

Light _____

Maximum	Deviation from standard	*Half*	Deviation from standard	*Light*	Deviation from standard
Trial 1 ____	_____	Trial 1 ____	_____	Trial 1 ____	_____
2 ____	_____	2 ____	_____	2 ____	_____
3 ____	_____	3 ____	_____	3 ____	_____

Table 10.2

Name _____	Date _____

Standard forces exerted: Non-preferred hand

Maximum _____

Half _____

Light _____

Maximum	Deviation from standard	*Half*	Deviation from standard	*Light*	Deviation from standard
Trial 1 ____	_____	Trial 1 ____	_____	Trial 1 ____	_____
2 ____	_____	2 ____	_____	2 ____	_____
3 ____	_____	3 ____	_____	3 ____	_____

QUESTIONS AND INFERENCES

1. Was there any difference between the results obtained with the preferred hand and the non-preferred hand? Can you offer any explanation?

2. Were results obtained consistent throughout the range? Would you expect similar kinds of errors on other psychomotor tasks?

3. Can one come closer to repeating a given amount of force if that force is very small or very large or in the middle? Comment.

4. On which of the standard forces would you expect to be most consistent? Why?

REFERENCES

1. Bell, Virginia L., *Sensorimotor Learning.* Pacific Palisades, California: Goodyear Publishing Co. 1970.

2. Cratty, Bryant, *Movement Behavior and Motor Learning.* Philadelphia: Lea and Febiger, 1967.

3. Held, R., "Exposure-History as a Factor in Maintaining Stability of Perception and Coordination," *Journal of Nervous and Mental Disease*, 132: 26-32, 1961.

4. Hoff, Phyllis A., "Scales of Selected Aspects of Kinesthesis," *Perception and Psychophysics*, 1971, Vol. 9 (1B), 118-120.

5. Lincoln, R., "Learning and Retaining a Rate of Movement with Aid of Kinesthetic and Verbal Cues," *Journal of Experimental Psychology*, 51: 199-204, 1956.

6. Smith, Judith, "Kinesthesis: A Model for Movement Feedback," in *New Perspectives of Man in Action*, B Cratty and R. Brown (eds.). Englewood Cliffs, N.J.: Prentice-Hall, 1969.

7. Steinhaus, Arthur H., "Your Muscles See More Than Your Eyes," *Journal of Health, Physical Education and Recreation*, 37: 38-40, 1966.

8. Weibe, V.R., "Study of Tests of Kinesthesis," *Research Quarterly*, 35: 222-230, 1954.

11

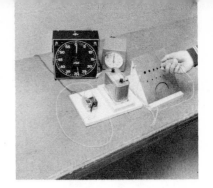

The Effect of Exercise
on Steadiness

Ataxia or body sway is a natural phenomenon that occurs because of constant checks and balances that are reflexively placed on our postural system. In addition, certain amounts of unsteadiness occurs due to such factors as fatigue, tension, etc.

When the entire organism is involved in strenuous exercise regimes this appears to stimulate the motor system in such a way as to exaggerate this lack of steadiness. The purpose of this experiment is to demonstrate this phenomenon.

PROBLEM

The problem is to determine the effect of strenuous exercise on general body and upper limb steadiness.

MATERIALS

Ataxiometer*, steadiness board**, 100th second chronometer, proper electrical circuitry.***

PROCEDURE

1. S stands in the ataxiometer for three thirty-second trials. Record the amount of "on balance" time.

2. Assuming a standing position, with arm held free of his body or any support, S starts with stylus in largest hole of the steadiness board, inserting the stylus approximately half way into the hole. With the metronome set at 60 per minute (1 per second) S holds the probe in each hole for ten seconds. One second is allowed for moving from one hole to the next. Record the total amount of "steadiness time."

3. S jumps rope for three minutes at as fast a rate as possible.

4. With no rest S repeats one and two above.

5. E and S change places and repeat one through four above.

RESULTS

Record results in the appropriate spaces in Tables 11.1 and 11.2.

---

* , **, ***, see Appendix.

Table 11.1 Steadiness Time-Ataxiameter

Ataxiameter	Before Exercise Balanced Time	After Exercise Balanced Time
Trial 1	_____	_____
Trial 2	_____	_____
Trial 3	_____	_____
Trial 4	_____	_____
Trial 5	_____	_____
Total:	_____	Total: _____

Table 11.2 Steadiness Time-Steadiness Board

Steadiness Board	Before Exercise Balanced Time	After Exercise Balanced Time
	_____	_____

DISCUSSION AND INFERENCES

1. Did the experiment result in less steadiness after a bout of exercise? Why?

2. What should we expect of elementary school children when they go back into a classroom following a vigorous recess period?

3. Can we say that motor activity relieves tension and generally relaxes an individual?

4. Is some amount of body and limb sway normal? Why (or why not)?

REFERENCES

1. Espenschade, Anna S., and Eckert, Helen M., *Motor Development* Columbus, Ohio: Charles E. Merrill, 1967.

2. Sage, George H. *Introductions to Motor Behavior: A Neuropsychological Approach* Reading, Massachusetts; Addison-Wesley, 1971.

3. Singer, Robert N. *Motor Learning and Human Performance: An Application to Physical Education Skills* 2nd Ed. New York: MacMillan, 1975.

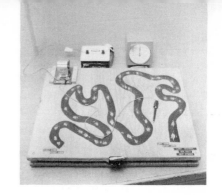

12

The Relationship Between
Speed and Accuracy

Some years ago "Poppelreuter's Law" was popularly assumed to best describe an aspect of learning. According to this "law," learning is enhanced if a task is practiced very slowly and accurately in the early stages and then speeded up when (and only when) accuracy is attained. Teachers of many types of motor tasks strictly adhered to this practice; "accuracy first" was an unquestioned principle. More recently this "law" was challenged and in many cases the old approach to learning many kinds of motor tasks has been shown to be inefficient. Now it appears that when speed is the most important or only component of a task, then practice in the early stages of learning should be at the greatest speed that can be controlled. Likewise, if accuracy is more important or the only component then accuracy should be the focal point of practice. Similarly, if a task requires a combination of speed and accuracy, then both should be emphasized throughout the learning process.

Since successful performance of most motor tasks commonly found in the area of sport and physical education requires both speed and accuracy, these components usually should be equally stressed throughout practice. It should always be remembered, however, that wild speed just for the sake of speed is not the object; *practice should be conducted up to the speed that can be controlled.* A tennis service or hockey slap shot, no matter how accelerated is, of course, of no value if not on target. By the same token even the most pin-pointed basketball pass is likely to be intercepted if thrown without adequate speed. The learner should practice from the beginning that which is required for successful performance. To demonstrate this principle is the purpose of this experiment.

PROBLEM

The problem is to investigate the speed-accuracy relationship using (1) a mechanical device or (2) a paper and pencil test.

MATERIALS

A tracking board,* stylus, electrical counter, 100th second chronometer, proper electrical circuitry; and/or fifteen paper and pencil accuracy test targets, stop watch.

(Use either Procedure A or B, not both)

PROCEDURE A

1. Work in a group of three persons.

---

*This tracking board was originally designed by Darlene Kelly. See Appendix.

2. S^1 stands in front of the apparatus with the stylus in the preferred hand, depressing the microswitch with the stylus. When ready, S_1 releases the stylus from the start switch thus starting the timer, and moves it around the track. The S thrusts at each target once with the stylus as he moves through the marked path. The movement must be a definite thrust; the S is not allowed to drag the stylus across the targets.

3. S^1 tries to touch each target, but may thrust only once at each target. At the end of the track the S depresses the stop switch, thereby stopping the timer. S^1 is to try only for speed, that is, to traverse the track as fast as possible. Ten trials are given.

4. S^2 repeats as above except S^2 attempts to be very accurate, trying to hit each target as it appears on the track, paying little or no heed to the amount of time it takes to complete each trial. He works for accuracy alone. Complete ten trials.

5. S^3 repeats as above, combining his effort to be *both* as accurate and as fast as possible. Complete ten trials.

6. *Each* S then does five additional trials, emphasizing *both* speed and accuracy.

RESULTS

Record on Table 12.1 the total time in seconds and total number of targets hit on all fifteen trials. Find the mean score for the last five trials for each condition.

PROCEDURE B

1. S^1 sits at a table, pencil in preferred hand, test materials before him. E has stop watch.

2. At signal "Ready? Go!" S^1 begins with circle number one and proceeds as rapidly as possible in numerical order, placing a pencilled dot in each circle. Only one attempt may be made at each circle. Ten trials are given. E times each trial with the stop watch. As in Procedure A, S^1 emphasizes accuracy in his practice, being sure to place a dot in each small circle, *regardless of traversal time.*

3. S^2 proceeds as above but disregards accuracy altogether, practicing the task *as fast as possible.* Ten trials are given.

4. S^3 repeats as above but stresses *speed and accuracy equally* in his practice. Ten trials are given.

5. *Each* S then completes five additional trials, *emphasizing both speed and accuracy.*

RESULTS

Record the total time and total number of targets hit on Table 12.2. Proceed as in Procedure A.

Table 12.1

S[1] Name _____			S[2] Name _____			S[3] Name _____		
Emphasis: Speed			Emphasis: Accuracy			Emphasis: Both		
	Hits	Time		Hits	Time		Hits	Time
Trial 1	___	1 ___	Trial 1	___	1 ___	Trial 1	___	1 ___
2	___	2 ___	2	___	2 ___	2	___	2 ___
3	___	3 ___	3	___	3 ___	3	___	3 ___
4	___	4 ___	4	___	4 ___	4	___	4 ___
5	___	5 ___	5	___	5 ___	5	___	5 ___
6	___	6 ___	6	___	6 ___	6	___	6 ___
7	___	7 ___	7	___	7 ___	7	___	7 ___
8	___	8 ___	8	___	8 ___	8	___	8 ___
9	___	9 ___	9	___	9 ___	9	___	9 ___
10		10	10		10	10		10
11	___	11 ___	11	___	11 ___	11	___	11 ___
12	___	12 ___	12	___	12 ___	12	___	12 ___
13	___	13 ___	13	___	13 ___	13	___	13 ___
14	___	14 ___	14	___	14 ___	14	___	14 ___
15	___	15 ___	15	___	15 ___	15	___	15 ___
Mean of 11-15:	___	___	Mean of 11-15:	___	___	Mean of 11-15:	___	___

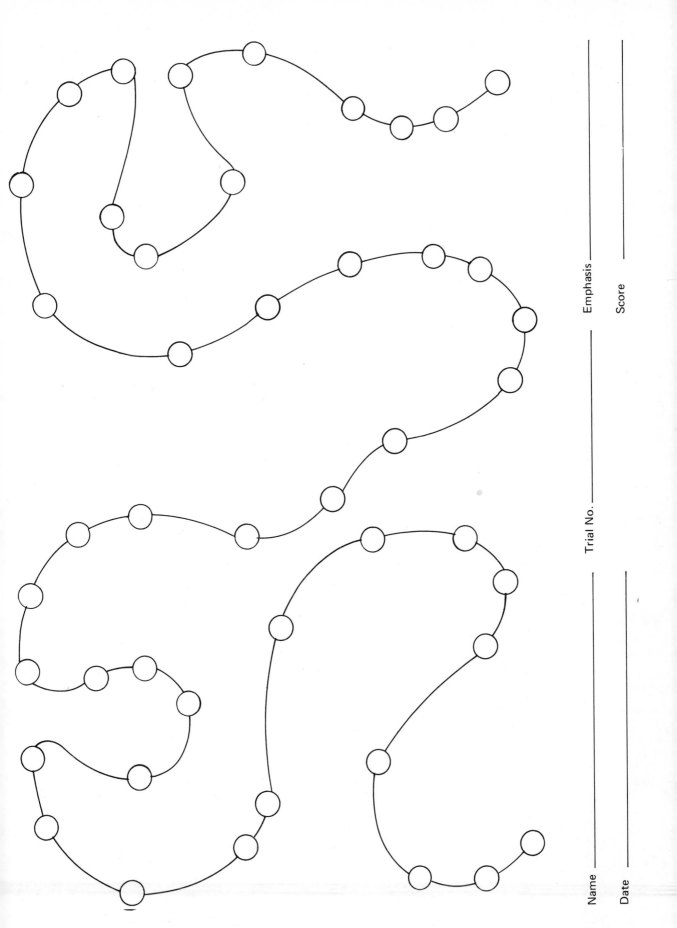

Name _____

Date _____

Trial No. _____

Emphasis _____

Score _____

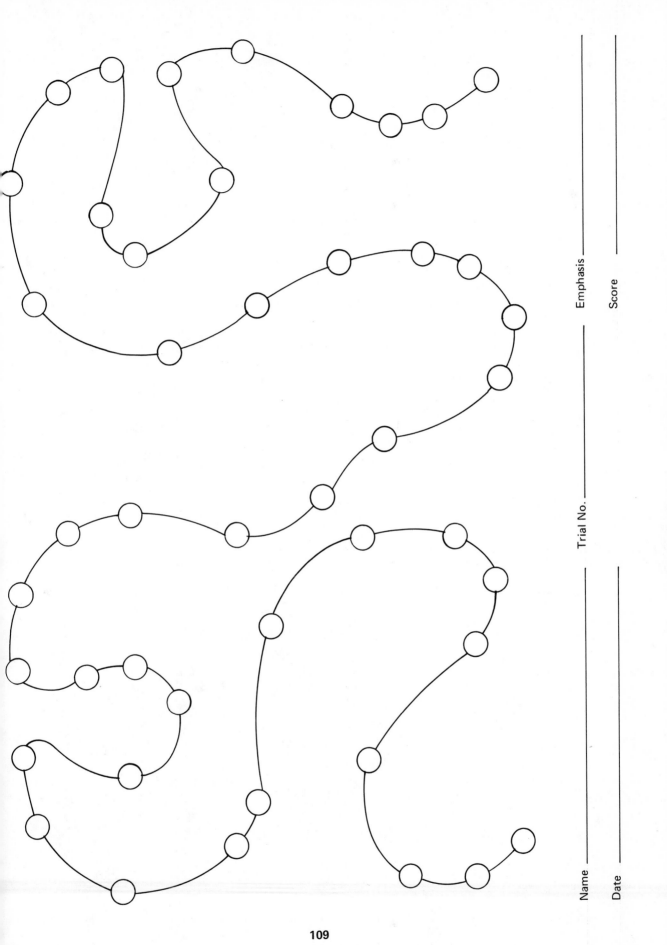

Trial No. _____

Emphasis _____

Score _____

Name _____

Date _____

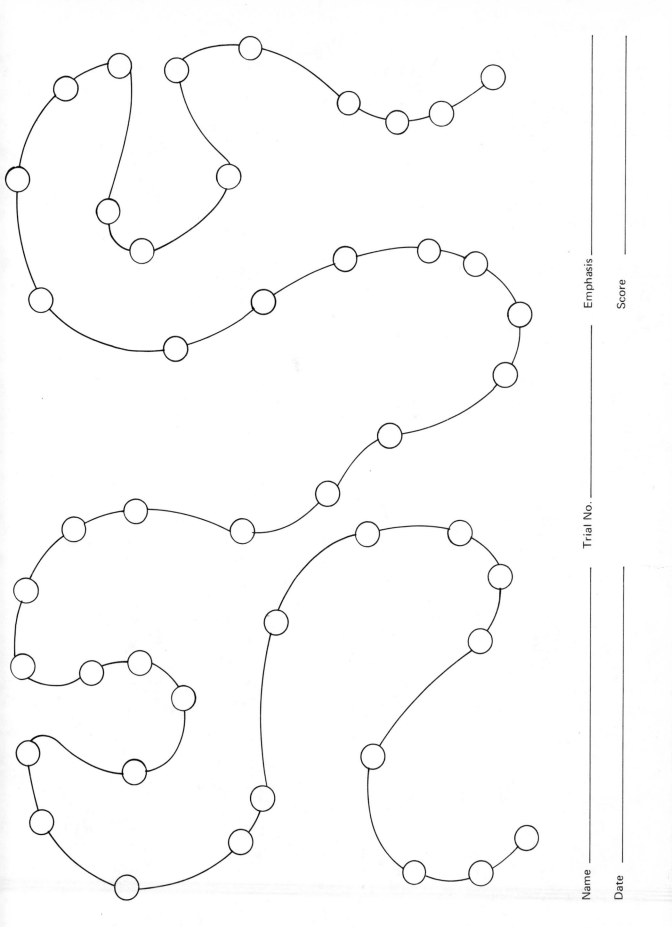

Name _____

Date _____

Trial No. _____

Emphasis _____

Score _____

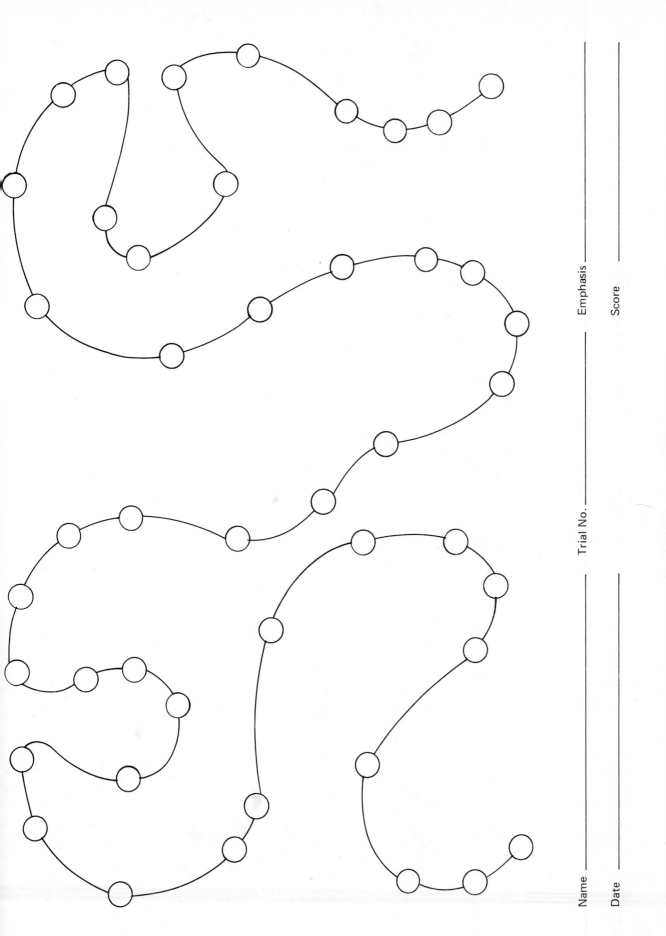

Name _____

Date _____

Trial No. _____

Emphasis _____

Score _____

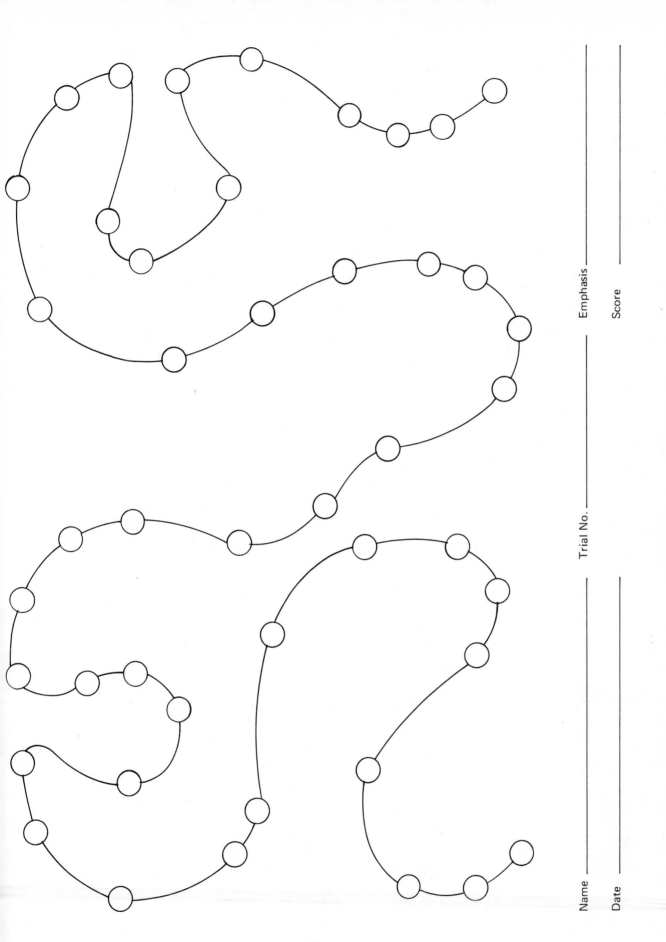

Name _____

Date _____

Trial No. _____ Emphasis _____

Score _____

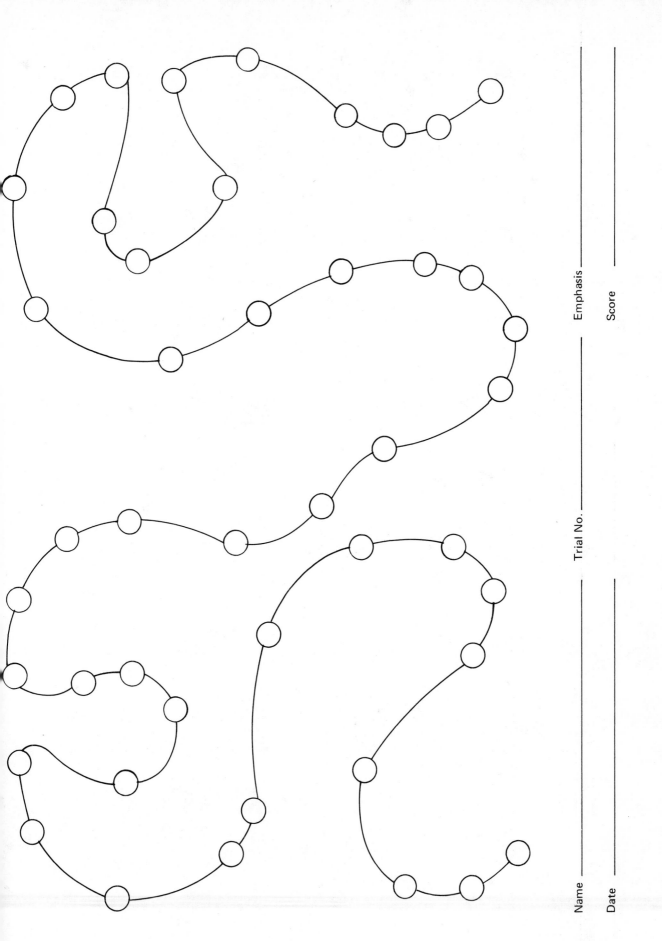

Name —————— Trial No. —————— Emphasis ——————

Date —————— Score ——————

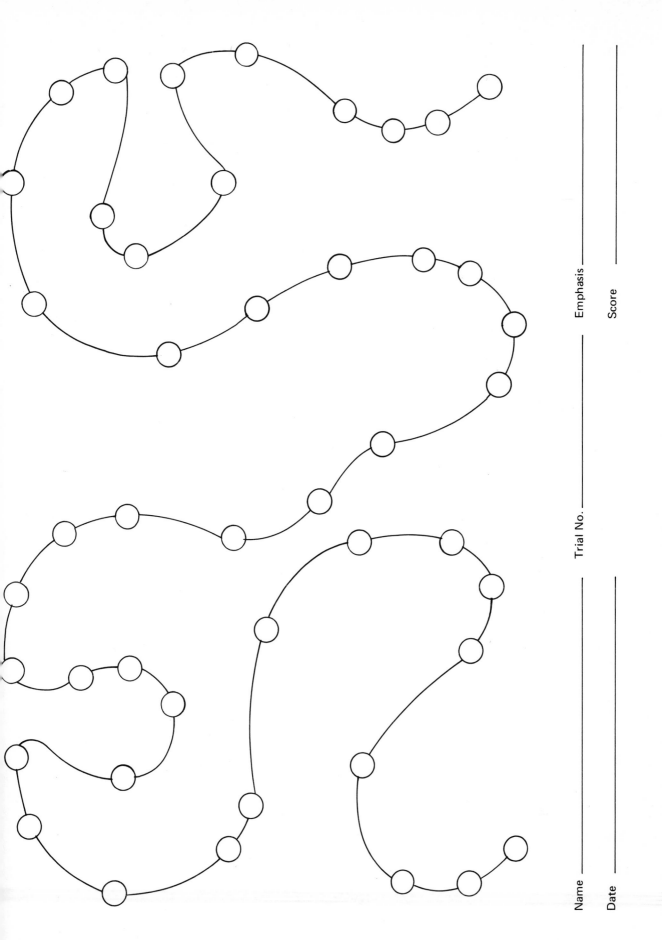

Name _____

Date _____

Trial No. _____

Emphasis _____

Score _____

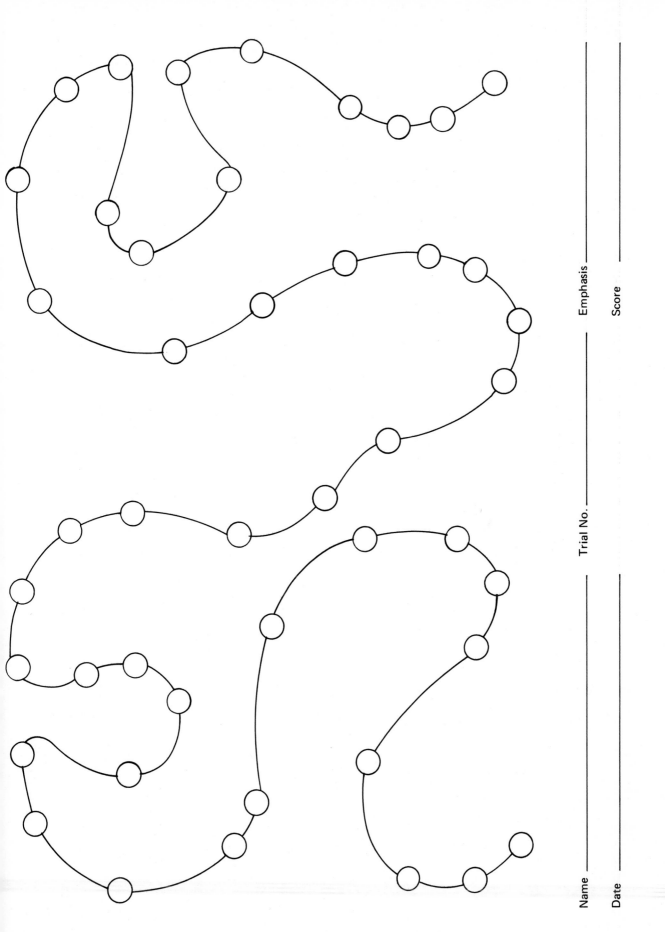

Name _____

Date _____

Trial No. _____

Emphasis _____

Score _____

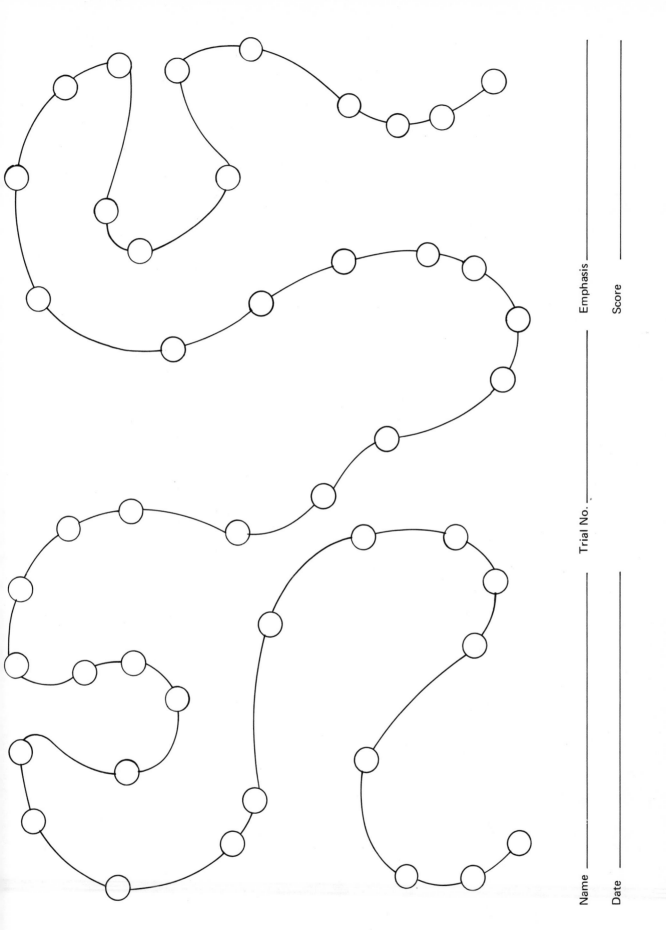

Name _____

Date _____

Trial No. _____

Emphasis _____

Score _____

123

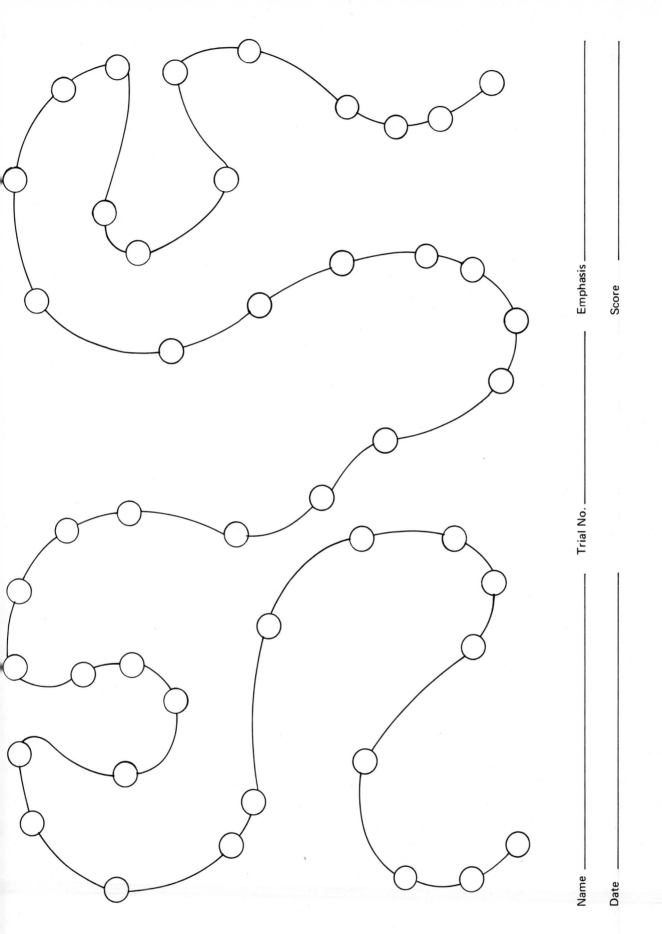

Name —————————

Date —————————

Trial No. —————————

Emphasis —————————

Score —————————

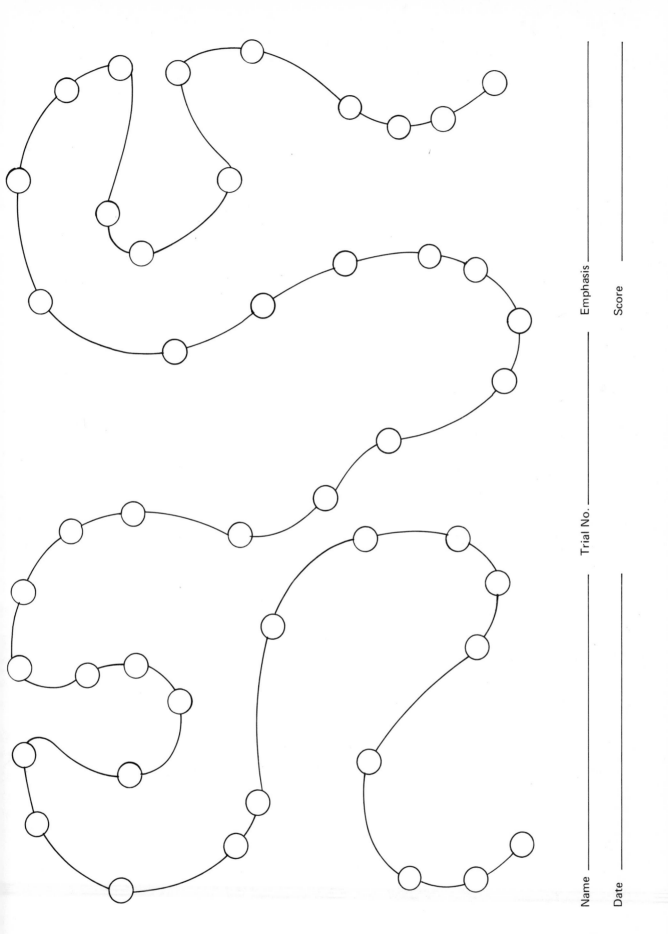

Name _____

Date _____

Trial No. _____

Emphasis _____

Score _____

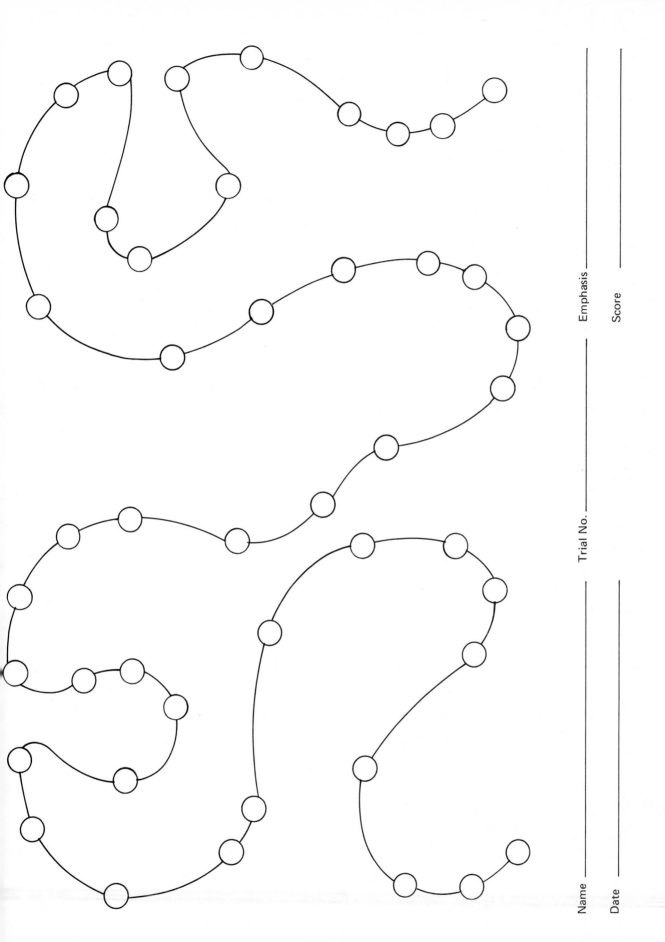

Name _____

Date _____

Trial No. _____

Emphasis _____

Score _____

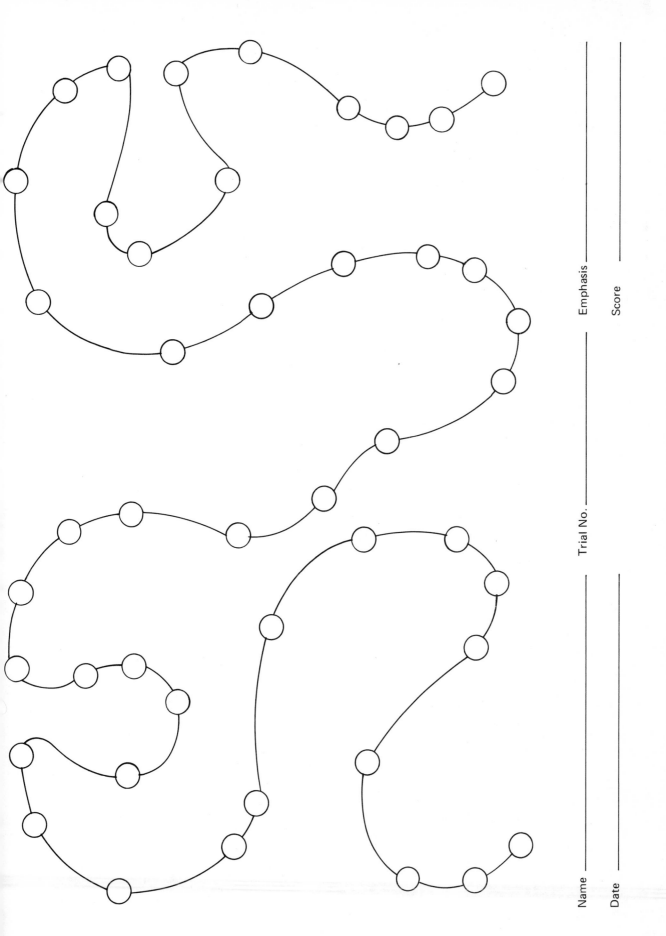

Name _____ Trial No. _____ Emphasis _____

Date _____ Score _____

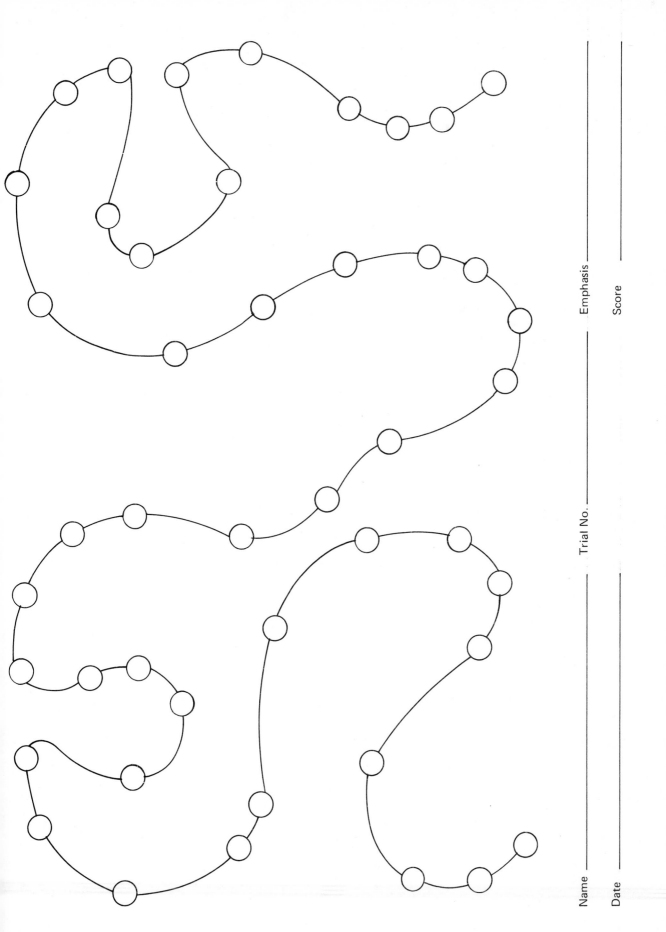

Name _____   Trial No. _____   Emphasis _____

Date _____   Score _____

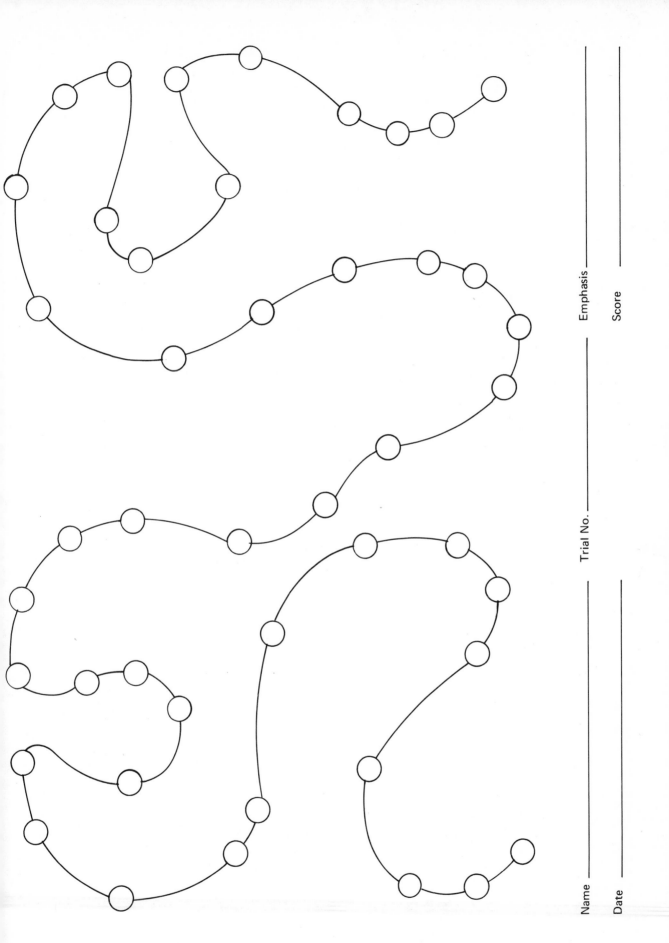

Name _____

Date _____

Trial No. _____

Emphasis _____

Score _____

Table 12.2

S¹ Name _____		S² Name _____		S³ Name _____	
Emphasis: Speed		Emphasis: Accuracy		Emphasis: Time	
Hits	Time	Hits	Time	Hits	Time
Trial 1 _____	1 _____	Trial 1 _____	1 _____	Trial 1 _____	1 _____
2 _____	2 _____	2 _____	2 _____	2 _____	2 _____
3 _____	3 _____	3 _____	3 _____	3 _____	3 _____
4 _____	4 _____	4 _____	4 _____	4 _____	4 _____
5 _____	5 _____	5 _____	5 _____	5 _____	5 _____
6 _____	6 _____	6 _____	6 _____	6 _____	6 _____
7 _____	7 _____	7 _____	7 _____	7 _____	7 _____
8 _____	8 _____	8 _____	8 _____	8 _____	8 _____
9 _____	9 _____	9 _____	9 _____	9 _____	9 _____
10	10	10	10	10	10
11 _____	11 _____	11 _____	11 _____	11 _____	11 _____
12 _____	12 _____	12 _____	12 _____	12 _____	12 _____
13 _____	13 _____	13 _____	13 _____	13 _____	13 _____
14 _____	14 _____	14 _____	14 _____	14 _____	14 _____
15 _____	15 _____	15 _____	15 _____	15 _____	15 _____
Mean of 11-15: _____	_____	Mean of 11-15: _____	_____	Mean of 11-15: _____	_____

DISCUSSION AND INFERENCES

1. Give three examples from teaching and coaching as applications of the principle demonstrated in the experiment.

2. Why do you think Poppelreuter's Law was ever accepted?

3. List two examples where accuracy in sports is imperative but speed immaterial, and give two examples where speed is essential but accuracy is of secondary or little importance.

4. Discuss pro and con the value of slow-motion demonstration and practice of motor tasks.

REFERENCES

1. Fulton, Ruth, "The Relationship of Speed and Accuracy in Motor Learning," *Research Quarterly,* 13: 330-36, 1942.

2. ——, "Speed and Accuracy in Learning Movements," *Archives of Psychology,* No. 300, 1954.

3. Knapp, Barbara, *Skill in Sport.* London: Routledge and Kegan Paul, 1963.

4. Oxendine, Joseph, *Psychology of Motor Learning.* New York: Appleton-Century-Crofts, 1968.

5. Singer, Robert, *Motor Learning and Human Performance: An Application to Physical Education Skills.* 2nd Edition New York: The MacMillan Company, 1975.

6. Smith, Hope (ed.), *Introduction to Human Movement.* Reading, Massachusetts: Addison-Wesley Publishing Co., 1968.

13

The Effect of Extended Practice on the Development of Skill

Although continued practice does not necessarily improve performance, motor skill gradually continues to develop if the performer is sufficiently motivated to persevere. Speed and efficiency grow better but advances come much more slowly at high levels of performance. Some fluctuations are to be expected but plateaus, contrary to customary opinion, are apparently not always inevitable. Learning need not end even though further improvement is difficult to achieve. There is no real asymptote or limit of learning (indicated by a horizontal levelling off of the curve) unless it (1) is physiologically induced, or (2) is defined by an investigator as the reaching of an arbitrary criterion (such as termination when subjects reach a predetermined point), or (3) is assumed (as when performers reach the point where they believe further progress is impossible), or (4) is inherent in the task itself (as when no further improvement is possible because the task sets the upper limit of ultimate rate or accuracy). From this experiment you should be able to observe the continuous nature of the development of motor skill. You will not observe this phenomenon unless you are the kind of subject (and investigator) who is sufficiently motivated to give "your all" on each day's trial, even when the extended practice otherwise might cease to be challenging. It is not necessary to have a great number of subjects to perform this experiment successfully. Even one or two subjects, if sufficiently motivated to "put forth their best" consistently during each of the many required trials, will be adequate.

PROBLEM

The problem is to investigate the effect of extended practice on the development of skill.

MATERIALS

Ball toss pegboard or standards*, twelve practice type handballs or six bean bags, an interval timer or stop watch, and a hand counter.

---

*A pegboard four feet long and six inches wide is hung at each end of a small room or between pillars in a room. Attached to each pegboard at one inch intervals are open eye bolts which are marked in terms of their distance, in inches, from the floor. Tightly strung between these boards is a rope which is attached to the eye bolts by means of snap hooks. Ordinary volleyball standards, usually marked in one-inch increments, may also be used. This task was devised by Waldean Robichaux and adapted by Joan D. Johnson and Joann M. Johnson.

PROCEDURE

1. Have the S stand with feet together, toes against the wall and forefingers of each hand together. From this position with the palms of the hands on the wall or pegboard, reach as high as possible. Note the height and add twelve inches to it. Then secure the rope at that height. Record this measure and use it for all ensuing practice for this subject.

2. Place a box with twelve practice-type handballs or six bean bags on the floor in front of the subject.

3. The S stands with a ball or bean bag in each hand under the rope and attempts to toss them simultaneously over the rope which is stretched twelve inches above his reach. Three twenty second trials (preceded by one fifteen second "warm up" trial) constitute one practice period.

4. Give the S one practice period on each of 10 consecutive days (or on all week days, or on some regularly established period of time during which it is possible to obtain the scores from at least 30 trials.

RESULTS

Score three points if both balls or bags are caught; if one is caught, one point is scored; if neither is caught, no point is scored. Balls that do not go over the rope are not scored.

DISCUSSION AND INFERENCES

1. Compare the nature and extent of fluctuations in performance during the beginning phase of learning with those of the intermediate and, finally, the most advanced stages of achievement.

2. Do you think it possible to improve your performance even further? If so, why; and if not, why not? What limits potential achievement?

Table 13.1 Improvement with Practice

Name of Subject: _____

Date: _____

TRIAL

Day	1	2	3	Total
1				
2				
3				
4				
5				
6				
7				
8				
9				
10				

Name _____

IMPROVEMENT WITH PRACTICE

3. If learning is defined as the development of dependable and responsible performance were you still "learning" during the latter days of practice? Do you agree with this definition?

4. Graph your results. Can you offer any explanation for the fluctuations?

REFERENCES

1. Bradley, James V., "Practice to an Asymptote?" *Journal of Motor Behavior,* 1: 285-295, 1969.

2. Fitts, P.M., "Factors in Complex Skill Training," in *Training Research and Education,* R. Glasser (ed) Pittsburgh: University of Pittsburgh Press, 1962.

3. Keller, F.S., "The Phantom Plateau," *Journal of the Experimental Analysis of Behavior,* 1: 1-13, 1958.

4. Snoddy, G.S., "Learning and Stability," *Journal of Applied Psychology,* 10: 1-36, 1926.

5. Stevens, J.C., and Savin, H.B., "On the Form of Learning Curves," *Journal of the Experimental Analysis of Behavior,* 5: 15-18, 1962.

14

The Orthogonal Effects
of Dynamic Balance

An extensive and carefully conducted factorial analysis investigation has indicated that the components of motor performance are often orthogonal.[5] That is to say that when all the bits and pieces of movement that result in motor performance are added together in proper sequence and magnitude, these specifics are not highly related to one another, either negatively or positively; the different parts are truly specifics, different factors. It has been suggested that the ability to balance is of this nature. Elsewhere in this manual (Experiment 17) one type of balance is illustrated: static balance. For tasks of this nature, the base balanced upon is stable. Two other suggested types of balance are the ability to balance objects, and the ability to maintain one's equilibrium during and after rotary movement, and these also seem to be orthogonal components of a more general balancing ability. Although static balance, object balance, and rotary balance are often required in motor performance, yet another type of balance seems to pervade in importance and that is dynamic balance. In this type of balance, the subject must attempt to maintain equilibrium while on an unstable base. In 1961, Bachman[1] compared two different kinds of tasks of dynamic balance and failed to find any significant relationship between them. Perhaps the ability to perform various balance tasks is even more specific than is generally supposed. The purpose of this experiment is to investigate general–specific aspects of performance.

PROBLEM

The problem is to compare performance on two tasks which are apparently quite similar in dynamic balance requirements.

MATERIALS

Dynabalometer,* proper electrical circuitry, 100th second chronometer, interval timer, free standing ladder,** stop watch, two or three large floor mats, hand counter. See note below.***

PROCEDURE A

1. S mounts the dynabalometer and is given a fifteen second practice trial.

2. E informs S of the results of the practice trial in terms of how much of the time S was able to maintain balance. E tells S that he is about to begin the first of five thirty second trials.

---

*This is a round platform, balanced on a "ball and socket" type trailer hitch. Its construction is described by Kenneth Penman in "A New Dynamic Balance Testing Device: The Dynabalometer," *Perceptual and Motor Skills* 23: 232-234, 1966.

**The free standing ladder is described by John C. Bachman in "Specificity in Learning and Performing Two Large Muscle Motor Tasks," *Research Quarterly*, 32: 3-11, 1961.

***The Bass Circle Test may be substituted for either the ladder or the dynabalometer. For a description see Ruth Bass, "An Analysis of the Components of Tests of Semicircular Canal Function and of Static and Dynamic Balance," *Research Quarterly*, 10: 33-52, 1939. See Appendix.

3. E sets the interval timer for thirty seconds and administers the five trials by saying to S: "Ready? Go!" to begin each trial and "Stop!" to end each trial. A 30-second rest is allowed between trials. After trial five E and S change places.

RESULTS

E records the total time balanced to the nearest one-hundredth of a second for each of the five trials on S's score sheet, Table 14.1. Record the total amount of time in balance during all five trials. The best three of these five scores are averaged and recorded on Master Data Chart.

PROCEDURE B

1. A large, well-matted area is necessary. S holds the ladder, on the matted area, by the sides at a comfortable height. The first rung of the ladder should be opposite S's left foot. Good footgear is essential to successful performance. At E's signal, "Ready? Go!" S places his left foot on rung number one and proceeds to climb the ladder, alternating feet, one rung at a time in order (rungs may not be skipped).

2. The ladder should be placed so that when S loses his balance, both S and the ladder remain in the matted area.

3. When balance is lost, S continues with as many attempts as possible during each thirty second trial.

4. E counts aloud the number of rungs attained on each attempt, keeping a record of the highest score for each trial.

5. Five thirty second trials are given with thirty seconds rest periods between trials.

RESULTS

The scores of the highest three attempts in each of the five trials are arranged and recorded on Table 14.2. The mean of these are placed on Master Data Chart. Record scores from at least ten class members and place on Table 14.3. Calculate r.

DISCUSSION AND INFERENCES

1. When scores obtained by at least ten members of the class on each task were tested for relationship what correlation (r) was found? Does this agree with Bachman's finding?

Table 14.1 (Dynabalometer)

S^1 Name _____	S^2 Name _____
Trial 1 _____	Trial 1 _____
Trial 2 _____	Trial 2 _____
Trial 3 _____	Trial 3 _____
Trial 4 _____	Trial 4 _____
Trial 5 _____	Trial 5 _____
Total of Best 3 _____	Total of Best 3 _____
Mean of Best 3 _____	Mean of Best 3 _____

Table 14.2 (Ladder)

S^1 Name _____	S^2 Name _____
Trial 1 _____	Trial 1 _____
Trial 2 _____	Trial 2 _____
Trial 3 _____	Trial 3 _____
Trial 4 _____	Trial 4 _____
Trial 5 _____	Trial 5 _____
Total of Best 3 _____	Total of Best 3 _____
Mean of Best 3 _____	Mean of Best 3 _____

Table 14.3 (Dynabalometer and Ladder)

Class Data

Class Member	Mean Score Dynabalometer (x)	Mean Score Ladder (y)	x^2	y^2	xy
1.					
2.					
3.					
4.					
5.					
6.					
7.					
8.					
9.					
10.					

Σx _____ Σy _____ Σx^2 _____ Σy^2 _____ Σxy _____

$$r = \sqrt{\frac{[N\Sigma xy - (\Sigma x)(\Sigma y)]^2}{[N\Sigma x^2 - (\Sigma x)^2][N\Sigma y^2 - (\Sigma y)^2]}}$$

$r =$

2. Do you agree that dynamic balance may have orthogonal components and that these are all but small parts of a general balancing ability? Explain.

3. Do you feel that either of the tasks done in this experiment can predict performance in such balancing-type sports as surfing, skiing, balance beam? Why, or why not?

4. Why do you think so much emphasis is placed on balancing-type activities in programs designed for children who have been diagnosed as having perceptual-motor difficulties?

REFERENCES

1. Bachman, John, "Specificity in Learning and Performing Two Large Muscle Motor Tasks," *Research Quarterly,* 32: 3-11, 1961.

2. Cron, G.W., and Pronko, N.H., "Development of the Sense of Balance in School Children," *Journal of Educational Research,* 51: 33-37, 1957.

3. Eldred, E., Granit, R., Holmgren, B., and Merton, P.A., "Proprioceptive Control of Muscular Contraction and the Cerebellum," *Journal of Physiology,* 123: 46-47, 1954.

4. Fitts, Paul, and Posner, Michael I., *Human Performance.* Belmont, California: Brooks/Cole Publishing Company, 1967.

5. Fleishman, Edwin, *The Structure and Measurement of Physical Fitness.* Englewood Cliffs: Prentice-Hall, Inc., 1964.

6. Godfrey, Barbara and Kephart, N.C., *Movement Patterns and Motor Education.* New York: Appleton-Century-Crofts, 1969.

7. Gross, Elmer A., and Thompson, Hugh L., "Relationship of Dynamic Balance to Ability in Swimming," *Research Quarterly,* 28: 342-346, 1957.

8. Johnson, G.B., "A Study in Learning to Walk the Tight Wire," *Pedagogical Seminary and Journal of Genetic Psychology,* 34: 118-128, 1927.

9. Stevens, S.S., (ed.), *Handbook of Experimental Psychology.* London: Chapman and Hall, 1951. (See especially chapters on "Sensory Mechanisms," "Motor Systems," and "Vestibular Functions.")

15

The Effect of Length of Set on Reaction Time

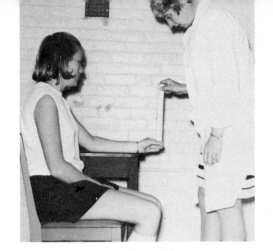

The delay between the presentation of a stimulus and the initiation of a response is known as reaction time. The speed with which humans can react is important in many sports situations and in everyday life. Reaction time is of great importance to scientists because it reflects the state of central process organization of an individual, hence it gives indication of the integrity of the nervous system.

As is commonly observed, the time necessary to react also varies because of the influence of such things as the nature and intensity of the stimulus, the level of attention and tension of the subject, his age, sex and motivation. Reaction time is also influenced by the sense organ that is the receptor of the stimulus, sound and touch resulting in faster reactions than do vision and pain. Another factor which influences speed of reaction is the preparatory "set" of the subject. If he is given a "ready" signal prior to presentation of the stimulus his reaction will be faster than it will be if he has no warning. A ready signal heightens the attentiveness of the subject preparing him for the ensuing stimulus. When this signal is given so that it precedes the actual stimulus by one to two seconds it has the greatest effect on shortening reaction time. Preparatory sets longer or shorter than this usually result in increased reaction times as it is the purpose of this experiment to demonstrate.

PROBLEM

The problem is to determine the effect on reaction time of varying the length of anticipatory set.

MATERIALS

Twelve inch ruler*, metronome.

Metronome

---

*The Nelson Reaction Time Ruler is a commercial device based on the formula given here and so automatically converts the distance an object falls into time. The present authors suggest that this experiment be performed, however, with a simple ruler as described here, believing that the experience of conversion, using the principle of falling objects, is more instructive.

PROCEDURE

1. Set the metronome at 120 beats per minute.

2. S is seated with preferred arm resting on a table at a comfortable height. S's hand extends just beyond the edge of the table.

3. E holds a ruler between S's thumb and forefinger with the scale on the ruler facing the thumb of S and S's thumb and forefinger one inch apart.

4. E holds the ruler at the top, lining up the eleven inch mark with S's thumb. With the metronome ticking at .5 second intervals, E says to S: "Ready?" and then drops the ruler at each of fifteen predetermined but randomized time intervals between the warning signal and the dropping of the ruler. (These intervals should range from .5 to 8.0 seconds and should be recorded on the score sheet, Table 15.1, *prior* to beginning the experiment).

5. Convert the number of inches that the ruler was allowed to fall before being caught on each trial to reaction time by the following method:

$$s = 1/2 \, gt^2 \; ; \text{therefore } t = \sqrt{\frac{2s}{g}}$$

(s = distance in inches (that the ruler falls); t = time (what you are looking for); g = acceleration due to gravity which is measured as 32 feet per second/per second). In order to convert inches to feet and therefore put s and g in the same parameter, use the following formula:

$$t = \sqrt{\frac{s}{6g}}$$

DISCUSSION AND INFERENCES

1. What implication do the results of this experiment have on the following sports situations:
   a. The time interval between "On Your Mark, Get Set, Go!" (gunshot).

   b. Similar interval between "Swimmers ready? Go!" (gunshot).

Table 15.1

Name of Subject _____ Date _____

Time Interval Between Warning and Stimulus (Randomly Predetermined)	Inches of Fall	Conversion of Distance into Time $t = \sqrt{\dfrac{s}{6g}}$
Trial 1 _____ seconds	Trial 1 _____	_____
2 _____ seconds	2 _____	_____
3 _____ seconds	3 _____	_____
4 _____ seconds	4 _____	_____
5 _____ seconds	5 _____	_____
6 _____ seconds	6 _____	_____
7 _____ seconds	7 _____	_____
8 _____ seconds	8 _____	_____
9 _____ seconds	9 _____	_____
10 _____ seconds	10 _____	_____
11 _____ seconds	11 _____	_____
12 _____ seconds	12 _____	_____
13 _____ seconds	13 _____	_____
14 _____ seconds	14 _____	_____
15 _____ seconds	15 _____	_____

c. The length of time between the first and second tennis service if the first serve is faulted.

2. Can reaction time be improved with practice?

3. List sports situations which specifically require fast reaction time.

REFERENCES

1. Adams, Jack A., and Creamer, Cyle R., "Proprioception Variables as Determiners of Anticipatory Timing Behavior," *Human Factors,* 4: 217-222, 1962.

2. Eason, Robert G., and White, Carroll, "Muscular Tension, Effort and Tracking Difficulty: Studies of Parameters which Affect Tension Level and Performance Efficiency," *Perceptual and Motor Skills,* 12: 331-372, 1961.

3. Gagné, Robert, and Fleishman, Edwin, *Psychology and Human Performance.* New York: Holt, Rinehart and Winston, 1959. ("Motor Skills and Response Capacities," 223-234).

4. Henry, Franklin, "Influence of Motor and Sensory Sets on Reaction Latency and Speed of Discrete Movements," *Research Quarterly*, 31: 459-468, 1960.

5. Henry, Franklin, "Reaction Time—Movement Time Correlation," *Perceptual and Motor Skills*, 63-66, 1961.

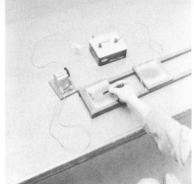

16

The Specificity of Speed

Speed, or rapidity of performance is necessary in a great many skilled acts. Speed is the ratio of the amount of work accomplished to the time required for its completion. In 1961 Smith[5] showed that both reaction time and movement time are highly specific to the limb and movement involved. It was suggested that there is a considerable amount of directional specificity when these parameters are thus assessed. The somewhat common tendency to refer to some individuals as "speedy" is not a completely clear or valid description. One may be able to move arm through flexion very quickly, for example, but be relatively slow when moving that same arm in extension. Likewise, one may be able to produce relatively fast extension of the elbow but not be able to exhibit this ability with knee extension. One may be a speed swimmer and a slow runner but speedy mobilization of effort is, nevertheless, important, in many competitive activities.

Some classify movement in terms of (1) fine and (2) gross; others as (1) discrete, and (2) continuous. Others categorize movement more precisely as (1) repetitive, (2) serial, (3) positioning, (4) pursuit, (5) reaction, and (6) steadiness. This experiment involves movement which can be called discrete and repetitive, illustrates fine and gross movement, and demonstrates the independent nature of speed of movement.

PROBLEM

The problem is to compare performance on two repetitive types of activities which have been purposely chosen as tasks for this experiment because of their similarity.

MATERIALS

Tapping plate,* counter, stylus, stop watch, proper electrical circuitry; two parallel lines drawn on the floor, 3/4 inches wide, three feet long and ten inches apart.

PROCEDURE A

1. S sits comfortably in front of tapping plate, stylus (held like a pencil) in preferred hand. Non-preferred hand and arm rests on the table, but *preferred hand should be free of support.*

2. E gives "Ready?" signal and starts the stop watch as he commands, "Go!"

---

*This is a complete circuit organized around an electric counter. The plates on the tapping board are connected, beneath the board, by a wire which also is connected to the counter by a wire from a pole on the counter. The other pole on the counter is connected to the stylus. When the stylus makes contact with one of the plates, the circuit is completed and the response is recorded. See Appendix.

3. At signal "Go!" S alternately taps each side of the tapping plate as rapidly as possible. The movement should be light and free, not a forceful thrust or jab. It must also be a true tapping motion, not a sliding back and forth of the stylus.

4. Three fifteen second trials are given with fifteen seconds rest between trials.

PROCEDURE B

1. The S is told that the object is to jump back and forth laterally across the space defined by the two lines, as rapidly as possible. He may try a few practice jumps.

2. S stands on either side of the space between the lines. At the signal "Ready? Go!" he jumps back and forth laterally across the space as rapidly as possible.

3. E counts the total number of contacts made when both S's feet are completely outside of the lines. S may step on the lines, but *not into the space* between the lines.

4. Three fifteen second trials are given with a one minute rest between trials.

RESULTS

The score of each trial is recorded on Table 16.1 and the total scores are added. Record your mean scores on the master chart so group data will be obtainable for all members of the class. Record data from ten class members on Table 16.2 and calculate r.

DISCUSSION AND INFERENCES

1. Using data from at least ten members of the class, calculate r. What correlation did you find between the speeds at which these two tasks were performed? What is the meaning of an r of this magnitude?

2. On the basis of the data do you think there is a meaningful relationship between the speed at which a single limb may be moved and the speed with which the total body can be moved?

Table 16.1

Tapping	Jumping
Name of Subject _____ Date _____	
Trial 1 _____	Trial 1 _____
Trial 2 _____	Trial 2 _____
Trial 3 _____	Trial 3 _____
Total _____	Total _____
Mean _____	Mean _____

3. Is the speed with which bodily parts can be moved specific or general? Can you base your answers on the results of this experiment?

Table 16.2 (Tapping and Jumping)

Class Members	Mean Score Tapping (X)	Mean Score Jumping (Y)	X²	Y²	XY
1. _____	_____	_____	_____	_____	_____
2. _____	_____	_____	_____	_____	_____
3. _____	_____	_____	_____	_____	_____
4. _____	_____	_____	_____	_____	_____
5. _____	_____	_____	_____	_____	_____
6. _____	_____	_____	_____	_____	_____
7. _____	_____	_____	_____	_____	_____
8. _____	_____	_____	_____	_____	_____
9. _____	_____	_____	_____	_____	_____
10. _____	_____	_____	_____	_____	_____

$\Sigma X =$ _____ $\Sigma Y =$ _____ $\Sigma X^2 =$ _____ $\Sigma Y^2 =$ _____ $\Sigma XY =$ _____

$$r = \sqrt{\frac{[N\Sigma XY - (\Sigma X)(\Sigma Y)]^2}{[N\Sigma X^2 - (\Sigma X)^2][N\Sigma Y^2 - (\Sigma Y)^2]}}$$

$r =$

4. What practical generalizations can you derive from this experience?

REFERENCES

1. Andreas, Burton G., *Experimental Psychology*. New York: John Wiley & Sons, Inc., 1962.

2. Crossman, E.R.F.W., "A Theory of the Acquisition of Speed-Skill," *Ergonomics,* 2: 153-166, 1959.

3. Lotter, W.S., "Interrelationships Among Reaction Times and Speeds of Movements of Different Limbs," *Research Quarterly,* 31: 147-155, 1960.

4. ———, "Specificity Versus Generality of Speed of Systematically Related Movements," *Research Quarterly,* 32: 55-62, 1961.

5. Smith, Leon, "Individual Differences in Strength, Reaction Latency, Mass and Length of Limbs, and Their Relation to Maximum Speed of Movement," *Research Quarteryly,* 32: 208-220, 1961.

6. Way, Eunice, Mott, Jane, and Lockhart, Aileene, "The Relationship Between Single Limb Movement and Total Body Movement in Six Types of Perceptual-Motor Performances," Unpublished study, University of Southern California, 1963. The demonstration presented in this experiment was devised for the above study by Way, Mott, and Lockhart.

17

The Effect of Vision
on Static and Dynamic Balancing Ability

Good balance is an extremely important factor in efficient motor performance. There appear to be at least three different and apparently independent balancing abilities: dynamic, rotational, and static balance. Static balance refers to the ability to achieve and/or maintain a state of equilibrium or steadiness in a desired position. As previously stated, in dynamic balance, the subject tries to maintain equilibrium while on an unstable base. Absence of movement is important in archery, in riflery, in the golf stance, in gymnastic and dance positions and good balance while moving is essential in basketball, skiing, bowling, etc.

Good motor performance requires the control of time, space, energy, and often objects, and good balance is a necessary prerequisite for this control and regulation. Balance, like reaction time, is basic because it is made possible through the integrity of several intricate physiological mechanisms which determine and direct the minute muscular compensations which check the extent of sway. The amount of sway varies with different persons and under different conditions. Although visual and vestibular senses are separate modalities the purpose of this experiment is to demonstrate the close relationship between vision and equilibration.

PROBLEM

The problem is to determine the effect of vision on static and dynamic balancing ability.

MATERIALS

A balancing stick board*, stabilometer** and proper electrical circuitry, interval timer, 100th second chronometer, stop watch, blindfold (or S may simply keep eyes closed).

PROCEDURE A

1. Ss should wear tennis or other gym shoes in order to participate in this experiment.

2. S places the ball of his preferred foot on the stick board with his foot crosswise with the stick. At E's signal, "Ready? Go!" the S attempts to balance in that position for as long as possible. (Do not exceed sixty seconds). When S loses his balance by stepping off the stick, or by placing the non-preferred foot or either hand on the floor, the trial is ended. AT NO TIME THROUGHOUT THE TRIALS should S lower the heel of the foot so as to touch the supporting base. Three trials are given, following one practice trial.

---

*This is a 1″ stick *securely* affixed to a larger board. It is recommended that the stick board be used on a rug or rubberized surface so that it cannot slip. The subject should be carefully spotted throughout the experiment since he is blindfolded. The stick board was first described by Ruth Bass in "An Analysis of the Components of Tests and Semicircular Canal Function and of Static and Dynamic Balance," *Research Quarterly*, 10: 35: 52, 1939.

**See Appendix.

3. E records the amount of time that the S is able to maintain a balanced position on each trial.

4. E and S change places and repeat numbers one through three above.

5. Repeat the entire procedure numbers one through four above but this time with the S blindfolded (or with eyes closed).

PROCEDURE B

1. E should always act as spotter for S during this experiment, especially during the part when S is blindfolded (or his eyes are closed).

2. S places one foot in each area of the stabilometer platform, keeping his weight on one foot in a stable position. Each foot must be parallel to and at least six inches from the balance rod.

3. After setting the interval timer for a thirty second period of time, E gives the signal "Ready? Go!" As soon as S attains a balanced position E starts the interval timer. This will measure a thirty second interval and actuate the 100th second chronometer for this length of time.

4. Three thirty second trials are given with a thirty second rest between trials.

5. E and S change places and repeat one through four above.

6. S_1 then is blindfolded (or for safety purposes, merely closes his eyes) and repeats one through five above.

RESULTS

Record and total the balance time for each subject for both conditions in both Procedures A and B (eyes open and blindfolded) on Tables 17.1 and 17.2.

DISCUSSION AND INFERENCES

1. Compare your scores (eyes open and blindfolded) and discuss probable reasons for any differences in scores.

2. List activities you may deal with in teaching and/or coaching where balancing ability if of little or no importance.

Table 17.1 Bass Stick

Name of Subject _____ Date _____	
With Vision	**Blindfolded (or Eyes Closed)**
Trial 1 _____	Trial 1 _____
2 _____	2 _____
3 _____	3 _____
Total _____	Total _____

Table 17.2 Stabliometer

Name of Subject _____ Date _____	
With Vision	**Blindfolded (or Eyes Closed)**
Trial 1 _____	Trial 1 _____
2 _____	2 _____
3 _____	3 _____
Total _____	Total _____

3. Can you give "hints" or "tricks" which may help a person in holding his balance? What underlying reasons make your suggestions credible?

4. Is the ability to balance an inherent quality? How much improvement in balance can be made through systematic practice?

REFERENCES

1. Guyton, Arthur C., *Textbook of Medical Physiology*, W.B. Saunders Company: Philadelphia, 1966.

2. Seashore, C.E., and Ling, T.L., "The Comparative Sensitivity of Blind and Seeing Persons," *Psychological Monographs*, 25: 148-155, 1918.

3. Singer, Robert, *Motor Learning and Human Performance*. New York: The MacMillan Co., 1968. ("Basic Considerations in Motor Learning and Performance," 58-61).

4. Travis, Roland C., "An Experimental Analysis of Dynamic and Static Equilibrium," *Journal of Experimental Psychology*, 35: 216-234, 1945.

5. Weisz, S., "Studies in Equilibrium Reactions," *Journal of Nervous and Mental Diseases*, 88: 150, 1938.

18

Weight Discrimination

There are many instances in sport where subtle differences in the weights of implements and objects are considered crucial by performers. Tennis players may insist, for example, that they must have a "heavy" rather than a "medium" weight racket even though the difference between such rated rackets may be as little as one-half ounce. Baseball players have been known to give credit for radical improvement in their batting averages to the fact that they switched bats, even though the change was as little as from a forty ounce to a thirty-eight ounce bat (or vice versa). Golfers insist on having A, B, or C weight woods. Bowlers use balls of specific weight. Expert performers in general are sensitive to the weight of their equipment and choose equipment with reference to their own strength, weight, experience and preference.

Classic study of kinesthetic sensitivity was conducted through experiments involving lifted weights. It was eventually found that all of our sensory systems operate in a similar way on an approximate logarithmic basis, threshold differences depending on a fixed incremental intensity (called Weber's Law). In the case of weights, one weight must be two per cent heavier or lighter than another before a difference between the two can be perceived. This is termed the "Just Noticeable Difference" (JND). Although the constant of proportionality does not always prove to be true in all sensory dimensions or at the extremely high and low ranges of intensity of any one sensory modality, Weber's Law is accepted in a general sense. The purpose here is to determine the accuracy with which you can make judgments related to one kind of kinesthetic sensation.

PROBLEM

The problem is to test the ability to discriminate among weights and, incidentally, to put Weber's Law to an informal test.

MATERIALS

A set of discrimination weights,* stop watch.

PROCEDURE

1. Place the weights in a container on a table in front of the S in random arrangement. Tell S to remove the weights from the container and place them in order from left to right with the lightest to the far left. S uses his preferred hand. Three forty-five second trials are given.

---

*Though available commercially, a set of cartridges or plastic containers, identical in appearance but varying in weight can be assembled with the aid of a pharmacist. The ten cylinders should be precisely weighted and coded as follows: A = 1/8 ounce; B = 1/4 ounce; C = 3/8 ounce; D = 1/2 ounce; E = 3/4 ounce; F = 7/8 ounce; G = 1 ounce; H = 1 1/2 ounces; I = 1 7/8 ounces; J = 2 ounces. These cylinders must appear identical, hence, the code numbers should be on the bottom.

1 gram = about 1/28 ounce; 1 grain = 0.0648 gram. These cylinders must appear identical, hence, the code numbers should be on the bottom. Use of melted parafin (included in the suggested weights) prevents auditory cues should subjects shake the cylinders.

2. Repeat above using non-preferred hand.

3. Repeat number one above allowing S to use either or both hands as he wishes.

4. Between trials, E replaces the cylinders in the container in a random fashion.

RESULTS

Record and total the correct number of relationships for all trials. To be correct, a cylinder must be in its proper position and it must also follow the weight that is next lightest. Perfect score is nine on each trial. Example of scoring:

A B C E D G F H I J

1 2   3 4

Table 18.1

Name _____ Date _____

Preferred Hand	Non-Preferred Hand	Either (or both) Hands
Trial 1 _____	Trial 1 _____	Trial 1 _____
2 _____	2 _____	2 _____
3 _____	3 _____	3 _____
Total _____	Total _____	Total _____

DISCUSSION AND INFERENCES

1. Did the results of this experiment demonstrate Weber's Law? Comment.

2. Compare the discriminatory ability of excellent tennis players with that of persons unskilled in tennis (a) on ability to judge weights of rackets, (b) on ability to judge the order of the ten cylinder weights.

3. Do you believe that perceptual ability in general can be learned? Can specific perceptual ability be improved?

4. Do you believe that there is a sex difference in relation to the ability to learn tasks which require kinesthetic information?

REFERENCES

1. Espenschade, Anna, "Kinesthetic Awareness in Motor Learning," *Perceptual and Motor Skills,* 8: 142, 1958.

2. Hoff, Phyllis A., "Scales of Selected Aspects of Kinesthesis," *Perception and Psychophysics* 1971, Vol. 9 (1B), 118-120.

3. Pillsubry, W.B., "Does the Sensation of Movement Originate in the Joint?" *American Journal of Psychology,* 12: 346-353, 1901.

4. Smith, Judith L., "Kinesthesis: A Model for Movement Feedback" in *New Perspectives of Man in Action* Roscoe C. Brown, Jr., and Bryant J. Cratty, Eds. Englewood Cliffs: Prentice-Hall, Inc. 1969 Chapter 3.

5. Thorndike, E.L., "A Note on the Accuracy of Discrimination of Weights and Lengths," *Psychological Review,* 16: 340-346, 1909.

6. United States Department of Health, Education and Welfare. *The Child With Central Nervous System Deficit.* Children's Bureau, Welfare Administration: Washington, D.C. 1965.

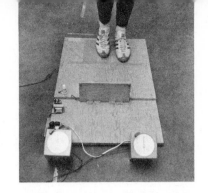

19

Movement and Reaction Times in Upper and Lower Limbs

In most areas of sport, aquatics and dance, combinations of coordinations are required between hand-eye, hand-foot, foot-eye, upper limbs-lower limbs. Yet it has been shown[4] that speed of movement is 87 or 88 per cent specific to each limb and even within a given limb speed of movement is 88 to 90 per cent specific to the direction of that movement. It is no wonder, then, that complicated motor tasks such as figure skating, skiing, basketball, and volleyball require years of hard practice. The purpose of this experiment is to demonstrate how reaction and movement times may vary from limb to limb, how reaction and movement times are specific to muscle groups and are not general to these groups.

PROBLEM

The problem is to compare upper and lower limb movement and reaction times.

MATERIALS

Foot reaction and movement timer apparatus*, hand reaction and movement timer apparatus, two 100th second chronometers, proper electrical circuitries.

PROCEDURE A
(FOOT REACTION AND MOVEMENT TIMER)

1. Work in groups of 2. S stands on board with both feet behind the microswitch. S places preferred foot so it depresses the foot button (microswitch). Place the kick board in full upright position.

2. E holds starting switch off and gives the command of "Ready." After one to four second interval he turns switch on which illuminates the light stimulus. Randomize the time between one to four seconds to prevent "jumping the gun."

3. When S sees stimulus light up, S moves the preferred foot from the foot button to knock down the kick board as quickly as possible.

4. Record the movement time (MT) and reaction time (RT).

5. Repeat the above procedure for 10 trials.

PROCEDURE B
(HAND REACTION AND MOVEMENT TIMER)

Use procedure (or data) from Experiment 2.

*See Appendix.

RESULTS

The score of each trial is recorded on Tables 19.1 and 19.2 and the total scores are averaged. Record these means on the master chart.

Using data from at least ten class members, record means on Table 19.3 and find r (correlation).

Table 19.1 Foot Reaction and Movement Time

MT	RT
1. _____	1. _____
2. _____	2. _____
3. _____	3. _____
4. _____	4. _____
5. _____	5. _____
6. _____	6. _____
7. _____	7. _____
8. _____	8. _____
9. _____	9. _____
10. _____	10. _____
Mean _____	Mean _____

Table 19.2 Hand Reaction and Movement Time

MT	RT
1. _____	1. _____
2. _____	2. _____
3. _____	3. _____
4. _____	4. _____
5. _____	5. _____
6. _____	6. _____
7. _____	7. _____
8. _____	8. _____
9. _____	9. _____
10. _____	10. _____
Mean _____	Mean _____

Table 19.3

Class Member	Upper Limb RT or MT (X)	Lower Limb RT or MT (Y)	X^2	Y^2	XY
1. _____	_____	_____	_____	_____	_____
2. _____	_____	_____	_____	_____	_____
3. _____	_____	_____	_____	_____	_____
4. _____	_____	_____	_____	_____	_____
5. _____	_____	_____	_____	_____	_____
6. _____	_____	_____	_____	_____	_____
7. _____	_____	_____	_____	_____	_____
8. _____	_____	_____	_____	_____	_____
9. _____	_____	_____	_____	_____	_____
10. _____	_____	_____	_____	_____	_____
	$\Sigma X = $____	$\Sigma Y = $____	$\Sigma X^2 = $____	$\Sigma Y^2 = $____	$\Sigma XY = $____

$$r = \sqrt{\frac{[N\Sigma XY - (\Sigma X)(\Sigma Y)]^2}{[N\Sigma X^2 - (\Sigma X)^2][N\Sigma Y^2 - (\Sigma Y)^2]}}$$

$$r = $$

QUESTIONS FOR DISCUSSION AND INFERENCES

1. Compare and explain the differences in results, if any, between the MT and RT of the upper versus lower limbs.

2. Using individual class averages for MT and RT, determine the coefficient of correlation between MT upper versus lower limb *or* RT upper versus lower limb.

3. What generalizations can be drawn concerning a relationship between RT and MR from upper to lower limbs (or vice versa)?

4. Would you expect any sex differences to appear that may affect the results of this experiment?

REFERENCES

1. Hodgkins, Jean, "Reaction time and speed of movement in males and females of various ages." *Research Quarterly* 34: 335-343, 1963.

2. Lotler, W.S., "Relationships among reaction times and speeds of movement in different limbs," *Research Quarterly* 31: 147-155, May, 1960.

3. Smith, Leon E., "Reaction time and movement time in four large muscle movements." *Research Quarterly* 32: 88-92, 1961.

4. ———. "Individual differences in strength, reaction latency, mass and length of limbs and their relation to maximal speed of movement." *Research Quarterly* 32: 208-220, 1961.

20

The Sequence of Practice
Whole versus Part

Considerable controversy has revolved around the question of whether things are best learned in "wholes" or in "parts" which, when put together, become "wholes." It is possible that the nature and effectiveness of practice may depend upon such things as whether the task is essentially serial or non-serial in type, the extent of its complexity, whether it requires simultaneous coordinations of two or more limbs, or whether it is basically of a motor or cognitive character. Sometimes practical situations dictate the type of practice engaged in, some "wholes" being simply too large or complicated to learn all at once (such as the games of football, field hockey, baseball). There are tasks, however, that simply cannot be parcelled into bits and consequently must be practiced wholly (such as learning to ride a bicycle). There are also occasions where the whole task may seem impossible until it is attacked in parts. The purpose of this experiment is to compare two methods of attacking a problem-solving situation: the one-thing-at-a-time or the part approach, and the complete unit or whole approach.

PROBLEM

The problem is to determine the relative effectiveness of using whole and part methods of practice while attempting to solve a problem.

MATERIALS

A problem solving peg board* with three pegs and seven discs of graduated length, and a stop watch.

PROCEDURE

1. The pegboard is placed before the S with the seven discs stacked on peg number one according to size, with the largest disc on the bottom.

2. S attempts to transfer the seven discs from peg number one to peg number three so that the discs are arranged on peg number three exactly as they were on peg number one. S may move any disc any number of times. He may use any peg. However, discs must be moved one at a time and no disc may ever be placed on a smaller disc.

3. E counts the number of moves made by the subject within a three minute trial.

---

*Though commercially available under the name "Burmese Pyramid" or "Pyramid Puzzle," this device can easily be constructed. It consists of a base on which are erected three posts or pegs and seven movable discs graduated in length. See Appendix.

4. If the S was not able to accomplish the task within the three minute period (and this will probably be the case), proceed as follows:

a. Set the pegboard up with only the top three discs on peg number one. The task remains the same: move the three discs from peg number one to peg number three, one at a time placing no disc on a smaller disc. Record the number of moves the S makes in solving this task and the time required to do so. Do not spend more than three minutes on any one portion of this task.

b. After the three disc problem is accomplished, add another disc. Record the number of moves and the amount of time required by the S in solving the four disc problem.

c. After the four disc problem is solved, add the fifth disc. Continue as above adding the sixth and seventh discs after accomplishing each of the prior, smaller tasks. In each case the E records the number of moves and the time necessary to accomplish the task using, in turn, three, four, five, six, and seven discs.

5. Repeat the whole procedure, one through four above, except that the E becomes the S.

RESULTS

Record the amount of time and the number of moves necessary to accomplish the task with three, four, five, six, and seven discs.

Table 20.1

Name of Subject _____ Date _____

In this experiment _____ was S_1

and _____ was S_2

Subsequent 3 Minute Trials:

Number of moves _____

Highest number accomplished _____

Original 3 Minute Trial:

	Time	Moves
3 discs	_____	_____
4 discs	_____	_____
5 discs	_____	_____
6 discs	_____	_____
7 discs	_____	_____

QUESTIONS AND INFERENCES

1. Of what value is trial and error on this task?

2. Of what value was E's mere observation of S's performance on the task? How does this fit in with the "We learn only by doing" theory?

3. Did you become frustrated on the original three minute trial? How did this affect your performance?

4. What sort of things occurred when you were doing this task that may be indications of insight? Were patterns or principles noted? Converse with other class members to ascertain whether these "Gestalts" were all mastered at about the same time. Comment.

REFERENCES

1. Bahrick, H.P., "An Analysis of Stimulus Variables Influencing the Proprioceptive Control of Movement," *Psychological Review,* 64: 324-328, 1957.

2. Fitts, Paul, and Posner, Michael, *Human Performance.* Belmont, Calif. Brooks/Cole Publishing Company, 1967.

3. Koch, H.L., "A Neglected Phase of the Part/Whole Problem," *Journal of Experimental Psychology,* 6: 366-376, 1923.

4. Lawther, John D., *The Learning of Physical Skills.* Englewood Cliffs, New Jersey: Prentice-Hall, 1968.

5. Neimeyer, Roy, "Part Versus Whole Methods and Massed Versus Distributed Practice in the Learning of Selected Large Muscle Activities," *College Physical Education Association Proceedings,* 61: 122-125, 1958.

6. Wickstrom, Ralph, "Comparative Study of Methodologies for Teaching Gymnastics and Tumbling Stunts," *Research Quarterly,* 29: 109-115, 1958.

Appendix
Some Sources of Motor Learning
Laboratory Equipment*

1. American Guidance Service, Inc., Publisher's Building, Circle Pines, Minnesota, 55014.
   Oseretsky Tests of Motor Proficiency, Minnesota Spatial Relations Test, Minnesota Rate of Manipulation.

2. Ann Arbor Instrument Works, 725 Packard Street, Ann Arbor, Michigan.
   Dynamometers.

3. Behavioral Science Products, Box 1176, Palo Alto, California.
   Makers of some popularized versions of problem-solving devices.

4. Bongo Corporation, 545 Fifth Avenue, New York, New York.
   Bongo board.

5. Bowmar Laboratories, 8000 Bluffton Road, PO Box 2835, Fort Wayne, Indiana, 46809.
   Computers, calculators.

6. Central Scientific Company, Cenco Center, 2600 Skostner, Chicago, Illinois, 60623.
   Counters, interval timers, stop clocks, stop watches, recorders, generators, galvanometers, physics apparatus.

7. Dekan Timing Devices, 295 Iowa Court, Carol Stream, Illinois, 60187.
   Automatic Performance Analyzer.

8. Dynalab Corporation, PO Box 112, Rochester, New York, 14601.
   Laboratory and educational research supplies.

9. E and M Instrument Company, Inc., Houston, Texas 77021.
   Physiograph, recorders, transducers, biotelemetry systems.

10. Elgin Exercise Appliance Company, PO Box 132, Elgin, Illinois.
    Progressive resistance exercise equipment.

11. Heath Company, Benton Harbor, Michigan.
    Do-it-yourself Heath kits.

12. Industrial Timer Corporation, Parsippany, New Jersey.
    "Time-O-Lite" and other timing devices.

13. Lafayette Instrument Company, Inc., PO Box 1279, Lafayette, Indiana, 479012.
    Sensory, perceptual, psychophysiological, motor, animal apparatus and equipment, timers and counters, learning devices, kinesthesiometer.

---

*Note list of instrument and equipment companies compiled by members of the Research Council of the AAHPER, printed in the *Research Quarterly*.

14. Lansford Publishing Company, PO Box 8711, San Jose, California, 95155.
    Educational and psychological transparencies.

15. Lee Lab Supply, Inc. 10009 West Arbor Vitae Street, Inglewood, California, 90301.
    Amplifiers, counters, galvanometers, oscilloscopes, strain gauges, telemetry systems.

16. Marietta Apparatus Company, 118 Maple Street, Marietta, Ohio, 45750.
    Perceptual, sensory, psychomotor, automatic reactivity devices, counters, timers, dynamometers, stability platform apparatus, general laboratory equipment.

17. M. Ducommun Company, 580 Fifth Avenue, New York, New York, 10036.
    Precision Minerva timers and stop watches.

18. Measurement Systems, 523 West Avenue South, Norwalk, Connecticut, 06854.

19. Meylan Stopwatch Corporation, 264 W. 40th Street, New York, New York, 10018.
    Stop watches, stop clocks, interval timers.

20. Minark Electric Company, 224 E. Third Street, Los Angeles, California, 90013.
    Electric motors, speed controllers, timers.

21. Pacific Games Company, North Hollywood, California.
    Labyrinthian maze, gravitation device.

22. Parker Brothers, Salem, Massachusetts.
    Card-sorting apparatus.

23. J.A. Preston Corporation, 71 Fifth Avenue, New York, New York, 10003.
    Treadmills, anthropometric devices, exercise equipment, Lincoln Oseretsky Motor Tests, depth perception, Purdue pegboard, metronomes.

24. The Psychological Corporation, 304 East 45th Street, New York, New York, 10017.
    Stromberg dexterity test, Crawford small parts dexterity.

25. Psychological Instrument Company, Box 6113, Richmond, Virginia, 23222.
    Chronoscopes, tracing boards, reaction apparatus, depth perception, steadiness testers, tachistoscope, mirror tracing boards.

26. Quinton Instruments, 3051 44th Avenue West, Seattle, Washington, 98199.
    Treadmills, bicycle ergometers.

27. Research Media, Inc., 4 Midland Avenue, Hicksville, New York, 11801.
    Pursuit trackers, visual perception apparatus, optical illusion kits, rod and frame devices, rapid rater.

28. Shaw Laboratories, Inc., 21 Harriet Drive, Syossett, Long Island, New York, 11791.
    Pursuit rotor, aesthesiometers.

29. Sierra Research Corporation, Box 22, Buffalo, New York, 11220.
    Radio, EKG, gymnastic apparatus.

30. Standard Electric Time Corporation, Springfield, Massachusetts, 01101; San Francisco, California, 94124.
    Precise time clocks of all kinds.

31. C.H. Stoelting Company, 424 N. Homan Avenue, Chicago, Illinois, 60624.
    Psychological and educational tests and materials, experimental research and recording apparatus, dynamometers, timers, mazes.

32. Takei and Company, Ltd., No. 18, 6-1 Chome, Hatanodai, Shinagawa-Ku, Tokyo, Japan, 142.
    Discrimination and illusion devices, reaction time, steadiness, pursuit rotors, dynamometers, sta-
    bilometers, trreadmills, metronomes.

33. Veeder-Root: Andrews Electrical Hardware, 1610 West 7th Street, Los Angeles, California.
    Precision counters of all types: hand tally, mechanical, electrical, photoelectric, speed indicators.

Suggestions for Construction and Use
of Motor Learning
Laboratory Equipment

As can be seen, some of the experiments suggested in this manual require little or no equipment for their completion. Others, however, do necessitate some rather sophisticated pieces of apparatus. The authors have found it necessary (either because the equipment was too expensive for available budget monies or because the equipment simply wasn't available commercially) to build much or all of this equipment from time to time.

Following are some practical suggestions for the construction and electrical circuitry of equipment of this type. An explanation of some symbols appears to be useful to persons who may be somewhat neophytes at endeavors of this nature:

AC—refers to the usual 110 volt alternating current available in most wall outlets. A three-pronged (hence, grounded) plug is suggested for use with this power source.

DC—refers to direct current power sources, usually 6 or 12 volt batteries. Other sources include various commercially available rheostatically controlled power sources that, though they plug into a 110 VAC circuit, convert this to direct current within a controllable range. A common 6 or 12 volt battery charger can be used in this manner as well as to serve its more obvious purpose.

K—symbol for relay switch. It is important that relays, when used, match up to the type (AC or DC) and voltage of the rest of the system within which they are used.

T—symbol for transformer. As with relays, transformers should match the remainder of the circuit scheme. Relays and transformers can be shorted out when carelessly used (plugged into an inappropriate power source, for example) so should be placed within easy access for replacement if and when this may be necessary.

⅋ —symbol for a light.

NO or NC—symbol for normally open and normally closed. These describe the position of a switch during which time it is inactive. These symbols are universally found on electrical components such as microswitched and electrical circuitry and should be attached according to instructions provided.

$||$ —symbol for power source. These are indicated on the following diagrams as 6 or 12 volts of direct current. The use of such DC batteries or other DC power sources sometimes appears to make the equipment cumbersome and complicated electrically. But it is one reason why various pieces of apparatus, quite expensive when commercially purchased, can be built and used for relatively sophisticated purposes, in motor learning laboratories that are on a meager budget.

Following is a description for the construction of the equipment necessary for the experiments in this manual:

Experiments 2 and 19—The Relationship Between Reaction Time and Movement Time and Movement and Reaction Time in Upper vs. Lower Limbs

The circuitry is diagrammed as follows:

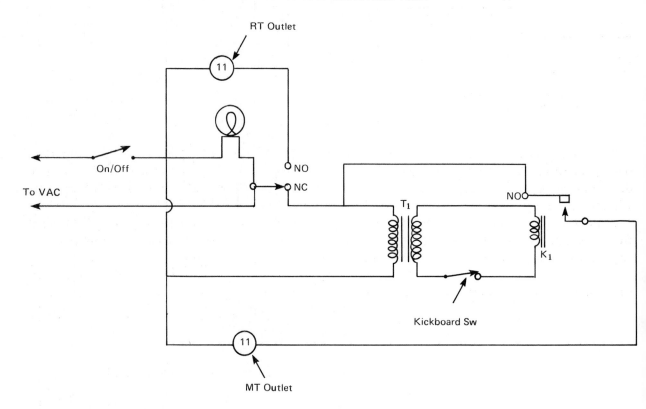

MOVEMENT AND REACTION TIME

T_1 — 120 VAC to 12 VAC

K_1 — Relay 12 VAC

The pieces of apparatus for measuring reaction time and movement time for either hand (arm) or foot (leg) are basically similar. The diagram above is for Experiment 19 but could be also used for Experiment 2 if built on a smaller scale and with a lighter "kickboard." The apparatus pictured for Experiment 2 utilizes an "electric eye" instead of a "kickboard." If funds for a photoelectric beam are available, it can be wired in exactly the same way as is the "kickboard."

100th second chronometers are necessary for these experiments and are plugged into outlets labelled "RT outlet" and "MT outlet." The on-off switch on each clock is left in the "on" position. The on-off switch controlled by the experimenter (which enables him to control the light stimulus) should be a silent mercury-type switch.

Experiment 6—Retention in Learning

PURSUIT ROTOR

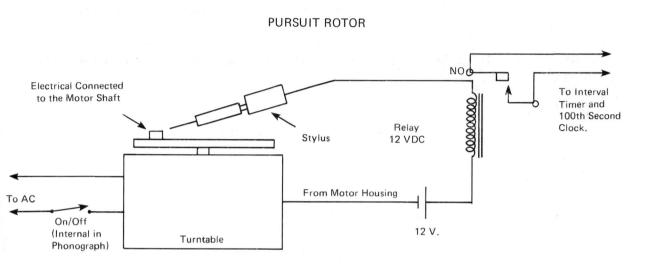

The above diagram shows how a phonograph turntable can be used as a pursuit rotor. A piece of beaver board should be cut in the same diameter as the turntable. The target can be inserted into this disc and connected to the motor shaft by a wire soldered to the target and to the shaft. Any metal disc will do for the target (a nickel works well).

A hinged stylus must be used or this task isn't difficult enough. These are commercially available from the Lafayette Company for about $25.00. The interval timer necessary can be purchased from any store that deals in photographic equipment for about $35.00.

Experiment 8—Augmented Knowledge of Results

MAZE

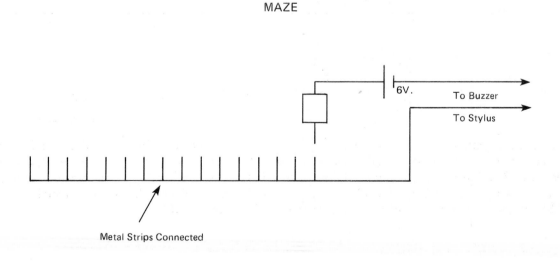

The pattern for a standard maze is cut out of half-inch plywwod with a saber saw. Cul de sacs are lined with metal plates which are wired to a buzzer. For the portion of the experiment that does not require augmented KOR, the buzzer is disconnected. A useable stylus for this experiment is a small screw driver cut off to about three inches in length. The shaft of the screw driver is wired, allowing the wire to run up the handle and secured there with electrician's tape.

Experiment 11—The Effects of Exercise on Steadiness

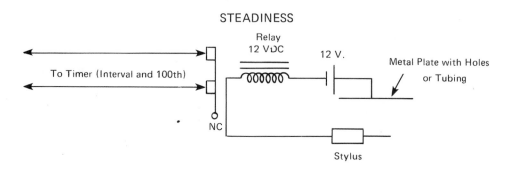

The same relay and power source can be used for both the steadiness board and the ataxiometer. The steadiness board is made from a piece of sheet metal into which holes are drilled of various sizes. The stylus for use with this board is made of a slender straight knitting needle, one end of which is inserted into large thermos corks. The corks are glued together (large end to large end) and serve as a handle for the stylus.

The target holes for the ataxiometer are four-inch lengths of copper tubing of various diameters. (1/2, 3/4, 1 inches). These should be mounted on a board which is then attached to the wall or some other sturdy upright that will allow for adjustments to subjects of various heights. The stylus for the ataxiometer is a short piece of solid copper shafting that is mounted to the top of an adjustable headpiece for a welder's helmet.

Either 6 or 12 volt DC power sources can be used, but in either case, the relay used should be of the same voltage as the power source.

Experiment 12—The Relationship Between Speed and Accuracy

SPEED AND ACCURACY

Micro Start Sw

S_1 S_2

On/Off   NC

To Timer

6 V.

To Counter

To Stylus

Nails All Connected

The speed-accuracy board is made of two pieces of half-inch plywood, separated by four dowels (1″) that are bolted to each of the four corners. Nails are driven into the board at various intervals within the pattern and the nails are connected by a wire to the 6 volt DC power source. The counter is connected to the other pole of the power source and the stylus to the counter.

The time necessary for each subject to complete the course of targets can be timed with a stop watch, or a 100th second chronometer may be wired to a 110 VAC microswitch that the subject activates and deactivates at the beginning and end of each trial.

The stylus may be made by wiring a steel shafted ball point pen to a 18-24″ piece of flexible wire. Be certain the pen has no ink supply remaining. Unscrew the shaft of the pen and run a short length of the wire (stripped of insulation) around the metal shaft of the insert five or six revolutions. Solder at the point and put the pen back together.

Experiment 14—The Orthogonal Effects of Dynamic Balance

DYNAMIC BALANCE

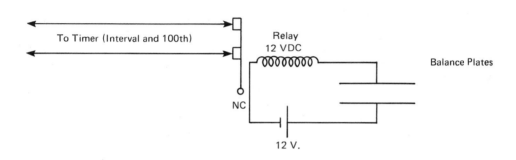

The balance platforms of the dynabalometer are constructed of round pieces of 3/4″ plywood that have continuous strips of sheet metal on their outside perimeters. The platforms are three feet in diameter. A round ball-type trailer hitch is mounted to the bottom platform and a block of hardwood is mounted to the top platform to receive the ball. The hardwood block is carved out to present a "seat" for the ball. (The ball should be greased periodically to insure free movement.) A 6 or 12 volt DC power source and relay are wired to the sheet metal plates as shown in the diagram. An interval timer and a 100th second chronometer complete the circuit.

Experiment 17—The Effect of Vision on Static and Dynamic Balancing Ability

STABILOMETER

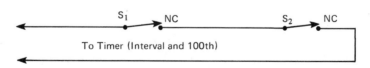

The base of the stabilometer is constructed to two pieces of triangular shaped 1/2″ plywood 18″ high and 38″ at the base. Between these, a balance platform 38″ × 21″ is suspended by a one-inch pipe. Stops are mounted on the base to prevent more than about three inches excursion up or down of 180°. Microswitches are mounted (S_1 and S_2 in the diagram) on these stops and connected to a 100th second chronometer and an interval timer in order to measure balance time.

DATA

NO. EXPERIMENT _____ NO. COURSE _____

TITLE _____

_____

NAME _____ DATE _____

1.									
2.									
3.									
4.									
5.									
6.									
7.									
8.									
9.									
10.									
11.									
12.									
13.									
14.									
15.									
16.									
17.									
18.									
19.									
20.									
21.									
22.									
23.									
24.									
25.									

DATA

NO. EXPERIMENT _____ NO. COURSE _____

TITLE _____

_____

NAME _____ DATE _____

1.										
2.										
3.										
4.										
5.										
6.										
7.										
8.										
9.										
10.										
11.										
12.										
13.										
14.										
15.										
16.										
17.										
18.										
19.										
20.										
21.										
22.										
23.										
24.										
25.										

DATA

NO. EXPERIMENT _____ NO. COURSE _____

TITLE _____

_____

NAME _____ DATE _____

1.									
2.									
3.									
4.									
5.									
6.									
7.									
8.									
9.									
10.									
11.									
12.									
13.									
14.									
15.									
16.									
17.									
18.									
19.									
20.									
21.									
22.									
23.									
24.									
25.									

DATA

NO. EXPERIMENT _____ NO. COURSE _____

TITLE _____

_____

NAME _____ DATE _____

1.									
2.									
3.									
4.									
5.									
6.									
7.									
8.									
9.									
10.									
11.									
12.									
13.									
14.									
15.									
16.									
17.									
18.									
19.									
20.									
21.									
22.									
23.									
24.									
25.									

DATA

NO. EXPERIMENT _____ NO. COURSE _____

TITLE _____

_____

NAME _____ DATE _____

1.									
2.									
3.									
4.									
5.									
6.									
7.									
8.									
9.									
10.									
11.									
12.									
13.									
14.									
15.									
16.									
17.									
18.									
19.									
20.									
21.									
22.									
23.									
24.									
25.									

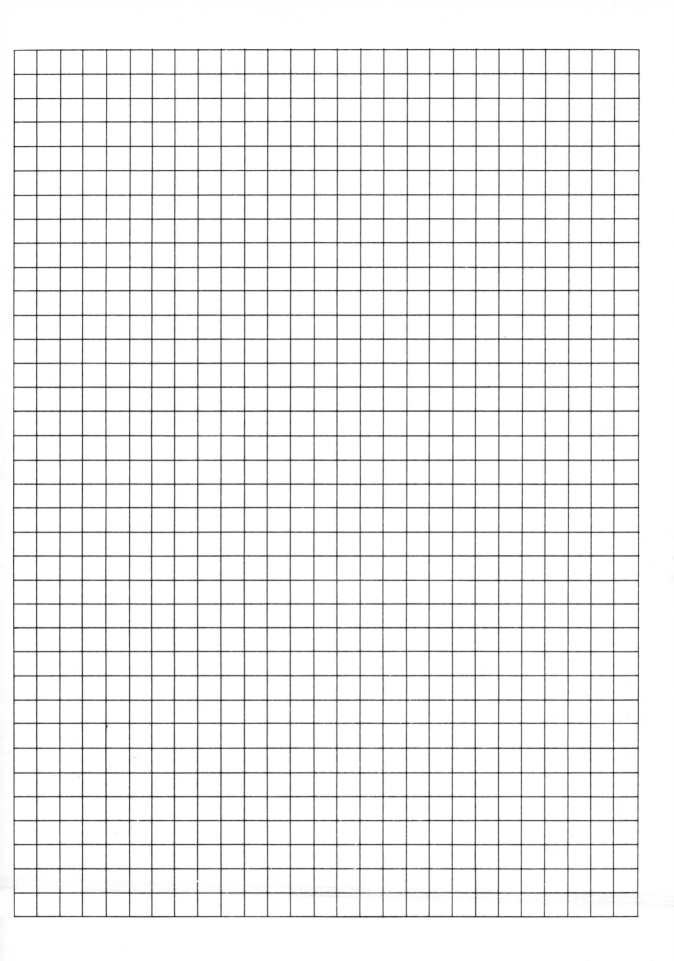

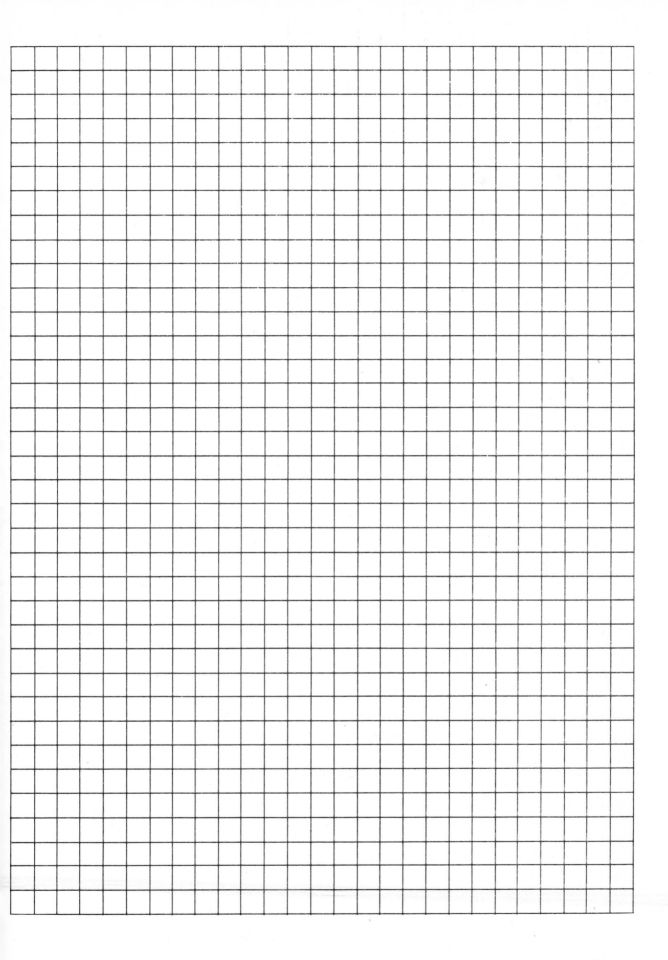

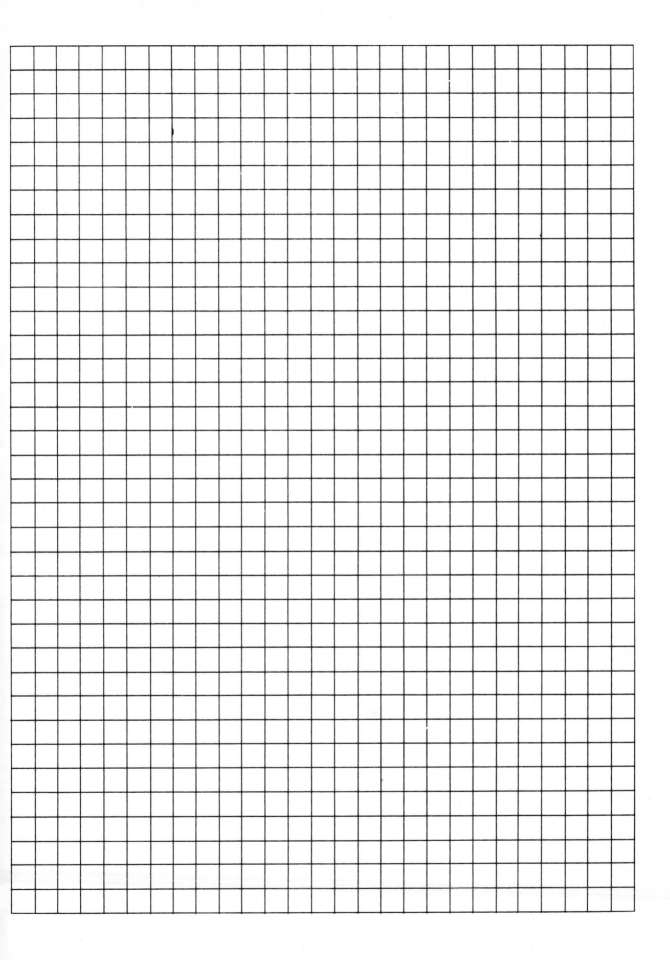

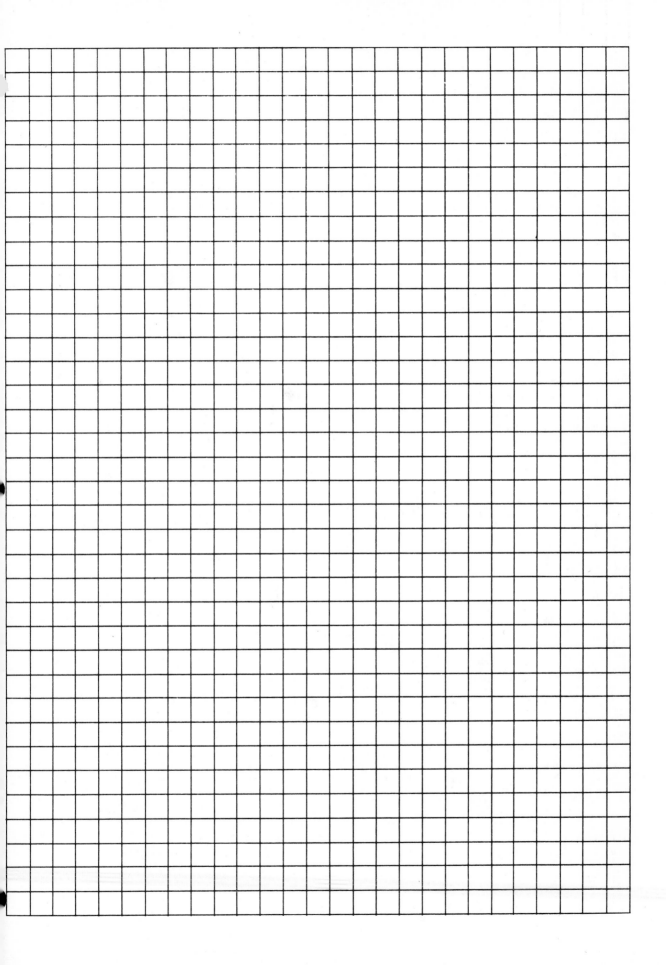

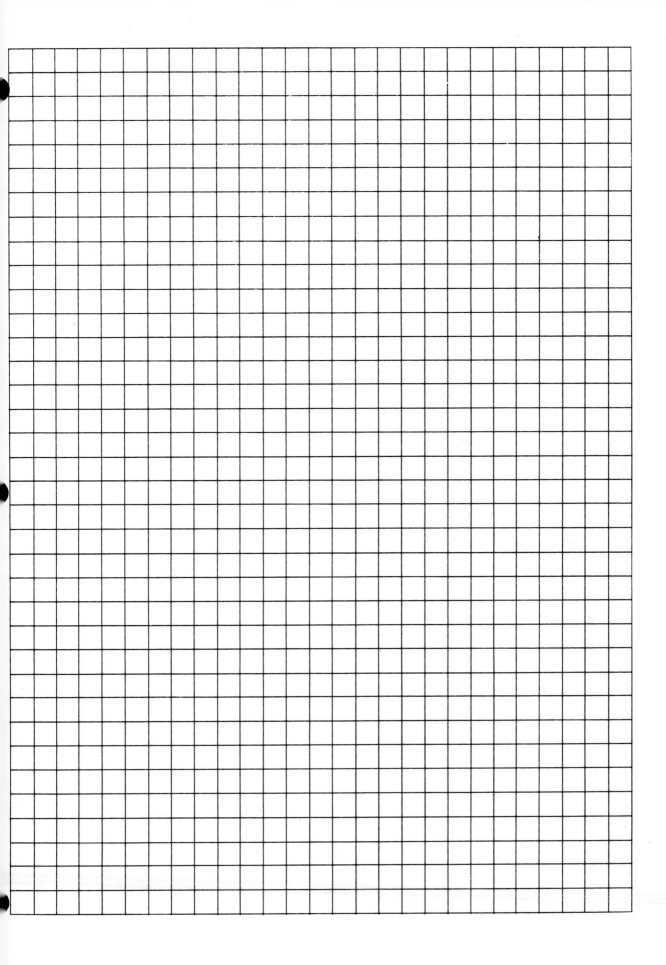

NOTES

NOTES

NOTES

NOTES

NOTES

Laboratory Experiments in
MOTOR LEARNING

Second Edition

Lockhart *and* Johnson

Kendall/Hunt Publishing Company
2460 Kerper Boulevard, Dubuque, Iowa 52001

C 401662

DATE DUE